Connected  Mathematics™

Comparing and Scaling

Ratio, Proportion, and Percent

Teacher's Guide

Glenda Lappan
James T. Fey
William M. Fitzgerald
Susan N. Friel
Elizabeth Difanis Phillips

Prentice
Hall

Glenview, Illinois
Needham, Massachusetts
Upper Saddle River, New Jersey

Connected Mathematics™ was developed at Michigan State University with financial support from the Michigan State University Office of the Provost, Computing and Technology, and the College of Natural Science.

This material is based upon work supported by the National Science Foundation under Grant No. MDR 9150217.

This project was supported, in part,
by the
National Science Foundation
Opinions expressed are those of the authors
and not necessarily those of the Foundation

The Michigan State University authors and administration have agreed that all MSU royalties arising from this publication will be devoted to purposes supported by the Department of Mathematics and the MSU Mathematics Education Enrichment Fund.

Photo Acknowledgements: 8 © Renee Lynn/Photo Researchers, Inc.; 17 © Peter Menzel/Stock, Boston; 18 © Peter Wandermark/Stock, Boston; 32 © Ralph Cowan/Tony Stone Images; 42 © Mitch Wojnarowicz/The Image Works; 45 © R. M. Collins, III/The Image Works; 50 © Erika Stone/Photo Researchers, Inc.; 52 © Lee Snider/The Image Works; 54 © Dion Ogust/The Image Works; 58 © John Coletti/Stock, Boston; 60 © Alvin Staffan/National Audubon Society/ Photo Researchers, Inc.; 65 © Peter Menzel/Stock, Boston; 79 © Don Rypka/UPI/Bettmann Newsphoto

Prentice
Hall

ISBN 0-13-053103-0

5 6 7 8 9 10   05 04 03

The Connected Mathematics Project Staff

Project Directors

James T. Fey
University of Maryland

William M. Fitzgerald
Michigan State University

Susan N. Friel
University of North Carolina at Chapel Hill

Glenda Lappan
Michigan State University

Elizabeth Difanis Phillips
Michigan State University

Project Manager

Kathy Burgis
Michigan State University

Technical Coordinator

Judith Martus Miller
Michigan State University

Collaborating Teachers/Writers

Mary K. Bouck
Portland, Michigan

Jacqueline Stewart
Okemos, Michigan

Curriculum Development Consultants

David Ben-Chaim
Weizmann Institute

Alex Friedlander
Weizmann Institute

Eleanor Geiger
University of Maryland

Jane Mitchell
University of North Carolina at Chapel Hill

Anthony D. Rickard
Alma College

Evaluation Team

Mark Hoover
Michigan State University

Diane V. Lambdin
Indiana University

Sandra K. Wilcox
Michigan State University

Judith S. Zawojewski
National-Louis University

Graduate Assistants

Scott J. Baldridge
Michigan State University

Angie S. Eshelman
Michigan State University

M. Faaiz Gierdien
Michigan State University

Jane M. Keiser
Indiana University

Angela S. Krebs
Michigan State University

James M. Larson
Michigan State University

Ronald Preston
Indiana University

Tat Ming Sze
Michigan State University

Sarah Theule-Lubienski
Michigan State University

Jeffrey J. Wanko
Michigan State University

Field Test Production Team

Katherine Oesterle
Michigan State University

Stacey L. Otto
University of North Carolina at Chapel Hill

Teacher/Assessment Team

Kathy Booth
Waverly, Michigan

Anita Clark
Marshall, Michigan

Julie Faulkner
Traverse City, Michigan

Theodore Gardella
Bloomfield Hills, Michigan

Yvonne Grant
Portland, Michigan

Linda R. Lobue
Vista, California

Suzanne McGrath
Chula Vista, California

Nancy McIntyre
Troy, Michigan

Mary Beth Schmitt
Traverse City, Michigan

Linda Walker
Tallahassee, Florida

Software Developer

Richard Burgis
East Lansing, Michigan

Development Center Directors

Nicholas Branca
San Diego State University

Dianne Briars
Pittsburgh Public Schools

Frances R. Curcio
New York University

Perry Lanier
Michigan State University

J. Michael Shaughnessy
Portland State University

Charles Vonder Embse
Central Michigan University

Field Test Coordinators

Michelle Bohan
Queens, New York

Melanie Branca
San Diego, California

Alecia Devantier
Shepherd, Michigan

Jenny Jorgensen
Flint, Michigan

Sandra Kralovec
Portland, Oregon

Sonia Marsalis
Flint, Michigan

William Schaeffer
Pittsburgh, Pennsylvania

Karma Vince
Toledo, Ohio

Virginia Wolf
Pittsburgh, Pennsylvania

Shirel Yaloz
Queens, New York

Student Assistants

Laura Hammond
David Roche
Courtney Stoner
Jovan Trpovski
Julie Valicenti
Michigan State University

Advisory Board

Pilot Teachers

Patricia Wagner
Holmes Middle School

Greg Williams
Gundry Elementary School

Lansing

Susan Bissonette
Waverly Middle School

Kathy Booth
Waverly East Intermediate School

Carole Campbell
Waverly East Intermediate School

Gary Gillespie
Waverly East Intermediate School

Denise Kehren
Waverly Middle School

Virginia Larson
Waverly East Intermediate School

Kelly Martin
Waverly Middle School

Laurie Metevier
Waverly East Intermediate School

Craig Paksi
Waverly East Intermediate School

Tony Pecoraro
Waverly Middle School

Helene Rewa
Waverly East Intermediate School

Arnold Stiefel
Waverly Middle School

Portland

Bill Carlton
Portland Middle School

Kathy Dole
Portland Middle School

Debby Flate
Portland Middle School

Yvonne Grant
Portland Middle School

Terry Keusch
Portland Middle School

John Manzini
Portland Middle School

Mary Parker
Portland Middle School

Scott Sandborn
Portland Middle School

Shepherd

Steve Brant
Shepherd Middle School

Marty Brock
Shepherd Middle School

Cathy Church
Shepherd Middle School

Ginny Crandall
Shepherd Middle School

Craig Ericksen
Shepherd Middle School

Natalie Hackney
Shepherd Middle School

Bill Hamilton
Shepherd Middle School

Julie Salisbury
Shepherd Middle School

Sturgis

Sandra Allen
Eastwood Elementary School

Margaret Baker
Eastwood Elementary School

Steven Baker
Eastwood Elementary School

Keith Barnes
Sturgis Middle School

Wilodean Beckwith
Eastwood Elementary School

Darcy Bird
Eastwood Elementary School

Bill Dickey
Sturgis Middle School

Ellen Eisele
Sturgis Middle School

James Hoelscher
Sturgis Middle School

Richard Nolan
Sturgis Middle School

J. Hunter Raiford
Sturgis Middle School

Cindy Sprowl
Eastwood Elementary School

Leslie Stewart
Eastwood Elementary School

Connie Sutton
Eastwood Elementary School

Traverse City

Maureen Bauer
Interlochen Elementary School

Ivanka Berskshire
East Junior High School

Sarah Boehm
Courtade Elementary School

Marilyn Conklin
Interlochen Elementary School

Nancy Crandall
Blair Elementary School

Fran Cullen
Courtade Elementary School

Eric Dreier
Old Mission Elementary School

Lisa Dzierwa
Cherry Knoll Elementary School

Ray Fouch
West Junior High School

Ed Hargis
Willow Hill Elementary School

Richard Henry
West Junior High School

Dessie Hughes
Cherry Knoll Elementary School

Ruthanne Kladder
Oak Park Elementary School

Bonnie Knapp
West Junior High School

Sue Laisure
Sabin Elementary School

Stan Malaski
Oak Park Elementary School

Jody Meyers
Sabin Elementary School

Marsha Myles
East Junior High School

Mary Beth O'Neil
Traverse Heights Elementary School

Jan Palkowski
East Junior High School

Karen Richardson
Old Mission Elementary School

Kristin Sak
Bertha Vos Elementary School

Mary Beth Schmitt
East Junior High School

Mike Schrotenboer
Norris Elementary School

Gail Smith
Willow Hill Elementary School

Karrie Tufts
Eastern Elementary School

Mike Wilson
East Junior High School

Tom Wilson
West Junior High School

Minnesota

Minneapolis

Betsy Ford
Northeast Middle School

New York

East Elmhurst

Allison Clark
Louis Armstrong Middle School

Dorothy Hershey
Louis Armstrong Middle School

J. Lewis McNeece
Louis Armstrong Middle School

Rossana Perez
Louis Armstrong Middle School

Merna Porter
Louis Armstrong Middle School

Marie Turini
Louis Armstrong Middle School

North Carolina

Durham

Everly Broadway
Durham Public Schools

Thomas Carson
Duke School for Children

Mary Hebrank
Duke School for Children

Bill O'Connor
Duke School for Children

Ruth Pershing
Duke School for Children

Peter Reichert
Duke School for Children

Elizabeth City

Rita Banks
Elizabeth City Middle School

Beth Chaundry
Elizabeth City Middle School

Amy Cuthbertson
Elizabeth City Middle School

Deni Dennison
Elizabeth City Middle School

Jean Gray
Elizabeth City Middle School

John McMenamin
Elizabeth City Middle School

Nicollette Nixon
Elizabeth City Middle School

Malinda Norfleet
Elizabeth City Middle School

Joyce O'Neal
Elizabeth City Middle School

Clevie Sawyer
Elizabeth City Middle School

Juanita Shannon
Elizabeth City Middle School

Terry Thorne
Elizabeth City Middle School

Rebecca Wardour
Elizabeth City Middle School

Leora Winslow
Elizabeth City Middle School

Franklinton

Susan Haywood
Franklinton Elementary School

Clyde Melton
Franklinton Elementary School

Louisburg

Lisa Anderson
Terrell Lane Middle School

Jackie Frazier
Terrell Lane Middle School

Pam Harris
Terrell Lane Middle School

Ohio

Toledo

Bonnie Bias
Hawkins Elementary School

Marsha Jackish
Hawkins Elementary School

Lee Jagodzinski
DeVeaux Junior High School

Norma J. King
Old Orchard Elementary School

Margaret McCready
Old Orchard Elementary School

Carmella Morton
DeVeaux Junior High School

Karen C. Rohrs
Hawkins Elementary School

Marie Sahloff
DeVeaux Junior High School

L. Michael Vince
McTigue Junior High School

Brenda D. Watkins
Old Orchard Elementary School

Oregon

Canby

Sandra Kralovec
Ackerman Middle School

Portland

Roberta Cohen
Catlin Gabel School

David Ellenberg
Catlin Gabel School

Sara Normington
Catlin Gabel School

Karen Scholte-Arce
Catlin Gabel School

West Linn

Marge Burack
Wood Middle School

Tracy Wygant
Athey Creek Middle School

Pennsylvania

Pittsburgh

Sheryl Adams
Reizenstein Middle School

Sue Barie
Frick International Studies Academy

Suzie Berry
Frick International Studies Academy

Richard Delgrosso
Frick International Studies Academy

Janet Falkowski
Frick International Studies Academy

Joanne George
Reizenstein Middle School

Harriet Hopper
Reizenstein Middle School

Chuck Jessen
Reizenstein Middle School

Ken Labuskes
Reizenstein Middle School

Barbara Lewis
Reizenstein Middle School

Sharon Mihalich
Reizenstein Middle School

Marianne O'Connor
Frick International Studies Academy

Mark Sammartino
Reizenstein Middle School

Washington

Seattle

Chris Johnson
University Preparatory Academy

Rick Purn
University Preparatory Academy

Contents

The broad purposes of this unit are to develop students' ability to make intelligent comparisons of quantitative information—using ratios, fractions, decimals, rates, unit rates, and percents—and to use quantitative comparison information to make larger or smaller scale models of given situations. An additional goal of this unit is not only to have students learn different ways to reason in proportional situations, but to recognize *when* such reasoning is appropriate.

Many important mathematical applications involve comparing quantities of one kind or another. In some cases, the problem is simply deciding which of two quantities is the greater and describing how much greater it is. In such instances, we subtract to find a difference. This is what students deal with in elementary school. In fact, since situations that call for comparison by addition or subtraction come first in students' experiences with mathematics, for many students this way of thinking becomes pervasive in any situation requiring comparison.

To compare two or more related measures or counts, such as 3 roses for $5 or 7 roses for $9, we need strategies that allow the related pairs of numbers to be compared. Simple subtraction will not tell us what we want to know. Here we enter the world of ratio and proportion. In this example, we need to find a way to scale the ratios of 3 to 5 and 7 to 9. Many students think these two ratios are the same, reasoning that 4 has been added to each of the numbers 3 and 5 to get 7 and 9. This is an example of students' misconceptions about when additive comparisons are appropriate. The price per rose, a rate comparison, in the 3 for $5 deal is $1.67. The price per rose in the 7 for $9 deal is $1.29—clearly the better price.

One of the recurring themes of these materials is that we can represent data in different ways and that each way may tell us something that is not as obvious from other representations. The comparison in the rose example can be made in several ways: for example, using unit rates (as was used above), comparing the ratios in fraction form to see which is larger, or scaling both rates until the price is the same or the number of roses is the same. Developing strategies for deciding what the comparison situation calls for and for making comparisons are major goals of this unit.

In the *Stretching and Shrinking* unit, the problem was finding dimensions of a larger (or smaller) physical or graphical model of some situation while preserving the *relative* size of the component parts so that the figures remained similar. The same ideas and ways of thinking developed in *Stretching and Shrinking* become powerful ways of thinking about ratios. The goal is the same in many ratio situations—to scale the ratios up or down so that one can see whether they are the same or different.

Another way the more numerical situations in *Comparing and Scaling* relate to the ideas in *Stretching and Shrinking* is that comparison problems often call for finding the missing part of a ratio equivalent to a given ratio, which is the same as solving a proportion. For example, suppose you have a rectangle with dimensions of 5 cm by 7 cm. You want to draw a larger, similar rectangle with the dimension corresponding to 5 cm being 15 cm. What would the other dimension be? This is identical to the question posed above: If roses are 5 for $7 and I want to buy 15 roses, how much will they cost? In each case, we are dealing with the given ratio of 5 to 7 and looking for the equivalent ratio of 15 to *x*. The *Stretching and Shrinking* unit precedes the *Comparing and Scaling* unit to give students prior experience with these ideas in a geometric context, which is more concrete than a numeric context.

The complex of concepts and skills in this unit is often referred to as proportional reasoning, and forming ratios in order to make comparisons is the heart of proportional reasoning. The unit starts with an investigation that raises issues about making comparisons. The next three investigations develop special ways of looking at comparisons—percents, ratios, proportions, rates, and unit rates. In the last two investigations, students apply these ideas in many kinds of situations, as part of the goal of this unit is for students to learn to make judgments about what kind of situation they are in and which comparing or scaling methods would be appropriate.

Mathematical and Problem-Solving Goals

***Comparing and Scaling* was created to help students**

- Use informal language to ask comparison questions, such as:

  "What is the ratio of boys to girls in our class?"

  "What fraction of the class is going to the spring picnic?"

  "What percent of the girls play basketball?"

  "Which model of car has the best fuel economy?"

  "Which long-distance telephone company is more popular?"

  "What proportion of the delegates should be from rural areas?"

- Decide when the most informative comparison is to find the difference between two quantities and when it is to form ratios between pairs of quantities

- Develop the ability to make judgments about rounding data to estimate ratio comparisons

- Find equivalent ratios to make more accurate and insightful comparisons

- Scale a ratio or fraction up or down to make a larger or smaller object or population with the same relative characteristics as the original

- Represent data in tables and graphs

- Apply proportional reasoning to situations in which capture-tag-recapture methods are appropriate for estimating population counts

- Set up and solve proportions that arise in applications

- Look for patterns in tables that will allow predictions to be made beyond the tables

- Connect unit rates with the rule describing a situation

- Begin to recognize that constant growth in a table will give a straight-line graph

- Use rates to describe population and traffic density (space per person or car)

The overall goal of the Connected Mathematics curriculum is to help students develop sound mathematical habits. Through their work in this and other number units, students learn important questions to ask themselves about any situation that can be represented and modeled mathematically, such as: *When quantities have different measurements, how can they be compared? When can a comparison be made by subtraction? When can division be used? Why is a ratio a good comparison? How can it be scaled up or down? How does rounding affect the numbers used in a ratio? What is the relationship between ratios and similar figures? Where can ratios be used in daily life to find unknown quantities or inaccessible measurements? How can we connect proportions and graphical techniques for solving problems?*

Investigation 1: Making Comparisons

Students encounter the language of comparisons and ratios in the context of advertising, which typically contains statements of comparison. They examine advertising claims for accuracy and their ability to convince. They informally explore strategies for presenting quantitative comparison information, particularly forming ratios. They analyze data and are challenged to form common types of comparison statements about the data.

Investigation 2: Comparing by Finding Percents

Students continue their exploration of comparisons with an emphasis on percents and the use of division for finding decimal or percent rates. Students have studied percents in depth in grade 6 in the Connected Mathematics curriculum, so this begins their study of proportional reasoning by building on what they already know. Students analyze data from a national survey on sports participation and find ways to describe or make comparisons among males and females and different age groups. They gather and analyze similar data from their own class and make comparisons between their data and the national survey data.

Investigation 3: Comparing by Using Ratios

Students explore typical recipe scaling problems and allocation problems to begin to develop strategies for scaling ratios to make comparisons or to find missing parts of equivalent ratios. This will remind them of their earlier work in mathematics of generating equivalent fractions. In fact, the thinking they will probably use here is the same as that used in finding equivalent fractions. Here, however, they are comparing quantities that refer to different kinds of measures, like tomatoes and money; with fractions, they were dealing with parts of a whole (the labels for the parts are the same).

Investigation 4: Comparing by Finding Rates

Students have used tables, graphs, verbal descriptions, and symbolic statements to represent data. Now they add the concepts of rates and unit rates to their strategies for reasoning about situations involving ratio and proportion. They look at situations in which making tables to explore rates is an efficient strategy for making comparisons. They search for patterns in their rate tables—regularities that help them to predict other numbers in the table. Observing patterns in tables and graphs will help students develop ways to tell whether a situation involves proportion. The unit rate is essentially the slope of the graph of a linear equation, which connects proportional reasoning and unit rates to students' earlier work with verbal descriptions, variables, patterns, algebraic rules, tables, and graphs.

Investigation 5: Estimating Populations and Population Densities

This investigation is a good connection to science and statistics. Now that students have some techniques for reasoning about ratios and proportions, they are introduced to real-world situations in which such reasoning is used. First, they consider how to estimate the size of a population when they do not have access to the entire population. They estimate the size of a crowd from a simulated photograph by counting the number of people in a small area and scaling up.

They simulate the capture-tag-recapture method for counting populations (as with wildlife monitoring). These two methods of predicting population counts from samples use reasoning with ratios and proportions. Then, students look at population densities—how much space per person or how many people per unit of space—and describe a population by giving its relationship to available area as a population density.

Investigation 6: Choosing Strategies

Students revisit proportional reasoning in a numerical as well as a geometric context. They focus on choosing appropriate strategies from the concepts and strategies they have developed during the unit to solve a variety of real-life proportional-reasoning problems. Often, more than one strategy can be used, so they are given practice in selecting an appropriate strategy.

The ideas in *Comparing and Scaling* build on and connect to several big ideas in other Connected Mathematics units.

Big Idea	Prior Work	Future Work
exploring proportional relationships between quantities	exploring and applying rational number concepts (*Bits and Pieces I; Bits and Pieces II*)	calculating and applying slope in equations of the form $y = mx + b$ (*Moving Straight Ahead; Thinking with Mathematical Models; Say It with Symbols*)
using percents to create a common scale for comparing two data sets (i.e., using percents allows you to express all quantities as values "out of 100")	defining percent as "out of 100"; connecting fractions, decimals, and percents (*Bits and Pieces I; Bits and Pieces II*)	making comparisons between groups of different sizes (*Data Around Us; Samples and Populations*)
interpreting fractions as ratios, as rates, or as comparisons of a part to the whole	interpreting fractions as part-to-whole comparisons; adding, subtracting, multiplying, and dividing fractions (*Bits and Pieces II; How Likely Is It?*)	expressing and applying probabilities as fractions (*What Do You Expect?*); determining whether two algebraic expressions are equivalent (*Say It with Symbols*)
scaling ratios up or down	comparing and subdividing similar figures to determine scale factors (*Stretching and Shrinking*)	scaling up rectangular prisms (*Filling and Wrapping*)
comparing quantities using ratios, rates, or percents	comparing fractions, decimals, and percents (*Bits and Pieces I; Bits and Pieces II*); comparing data sets (*Data About Us*)	comparing probabilities (*What Do You Expect?; Samples and Populations*); comparing data sets (*Data Around Us*)
developing techniques to estimate population densities and other quantities	making inferences about quantities and populations based on experimental or theoretical probabilities (*How Likely Is It?*)	estimating with and comparing large numbers (*Data Around Us*); developing benchmarks and skills for estimating irrational numbers (*Looking for Pythagoras*); estimating populations (*Samples and Populations*)

Materials

For students

- Labsheets
- Orange and white chips or squares of paper (optional; about 25 orange and 100 white per group)
- Containers (large enough so students can mix the contents) of 300–800 white beans, with lid
- Scoops for sampling (optional)
- Centimeter and inch grid paper (provided as blackline masters)
- Transparencies of centimeter and inch grid paper and transparency markers (copy the blackline masters onto transparency film)
- Graphing calculators
- Markers
- Large sheets of paper (optional)

For the teacher

- Transparencies and transparency markers (optional)
- Advertisements containing comparisons (optional)
- Can of orange juice concentrate and pitcher (optional)
- News article that reports an estimate of crowd size (optional)

Technology

We expect that students will use calculators freely to perform arithmetic computations so that their focus can be on analyzing the problems and searching for patterns. Connected Mathematics was developed with the belief that calculators should always be available and that students should decide when to use them. For this reason, we do not designate specific problems as "calculator problems."

Pacing Chart

This pacing chart gives estimates of the class time required for each investigation and assessment piece. Shaded rows indicate opportunities for assessment.

Investigations and Assessments	Class Time
1 Making Comparisons	4 days
2 Comparing by Finding Percents	2 days
Check-Up 1	$\frac{1}{2}$ day
3 Comparing by Using Ratios	3 days
4 Comparing by Finding Rates	4 days
Check-Up 2	$\frac{1}{2}$ day
Quiz	1 day
5 Estimating Populations and Population Densities	2 days
6 Choosing Strategies	2 days
Unit Test	1 day
Self-Assessment	Take home
Unit Project (optional)	2–3 days

Comparing and Scaling Vocabulary

The following words and concepts are used in *Comparing and Scaling*. Concepts in the left column are those essential for student understanding of this and future units. The Descriptive Glossary gives descriptions of many of these words.

Essential terms developed in this unit	Terms developed in previous units	Nonessential terms
population density	decimal	capture-tag-recapture method
rate	difference	constant
ratio	equation	proportion
scale, scaling	equivalence	
unit rate	fraction	
	graph, coordinate graph	
	percent	
	scale factor	

Embedded Assessment

Opportunities for informal assessment of student progress are embedded throughout *Comparing and Scaling* in the problems, the ACE questions, and the Mathematical Reflections. Suggestions for observing as students explore and discover mathematical ideas, for probing to guide their progress in developing concepts and skills, and for questioning to determine their level of understanding can be found in the Launch, Explore, or Summarize sections of all investigation problems. Some examples:

- Investigation 5, Problem 5.2 *Launch* (page 64b) suggests how you can help students understand how the simulation of the capture-tag-recapture method models the method actually used to estimate wildlife populations.

- Investigation 3, Problem 3.1 *Explore* (page 36a) suggests ways you can help students understand how the amounts of ingredients in a recipe relate to the proportion of each ingredient in the recipe and how these proportions might be modeled.

- Investigation 1, Problem 1.3 *Summarize* (page 15c) suggests questions you might ask to extend and assess students' thinking about comparisons that can be made among a given set of data.

ACE Assignments

An ACE (Applications—Connections—Extensions) section appears at the end of each investigation. To help you assign ACE questions, a list of assignment choices is given in the margin next to the reduced student page for each problem. Each list indicates the ACE questions that students should be able to answer after they complete the problem.

Partner Quiz

One quiz, which may be given after Investigation 4, is provided with *Comparing and Scaling*. The quiz is designed to be completed by pairs of students with the opportunity for revision based on teacher feedback. You will find the quiz and its answers in the Assessment Resources section. As an alternative to the quiz provided, you can construct your own quiz by combining questions from the Question Bank, this quiz, and unassigned ACE questions.

Check-Ups

Two check-ups, which may be given after Investigations 2 and 4, are provided for use as quick quizzes or warm-up activities. The check-ups are designed for students to complete individually. You will find the check-ups and their answer keys in the Assessment Resources section.

Question Bank

A Question Bank provides questions you can use for homework, reviews, or quizzes. You will find the Question Bank and its answer key in the Assessment Resources section.

Notebook/Journal

Students should have notebooks to record and organize their work. Notebooks should include student journals and sections for vocabulary, homework, and quizzes and check-ups. In their journals, students can take notes, solve investigation problems, write down ideas for their projects, and record their ideas about Mathematical Reflections questions. Journals should be assessed for completeness rather than correctness; they should be seen as "safe" places where students can try out their thinking. A Notebook Checklist and a Self-Assessment are provided in the Assessment Resources section. The Notebook Checklist helps students organize their notebooks. The Self-Assessment guides students as they review their notebooks to determine which ideas they have mastered and which they still need to work on.

The Unit Test

The assessment for *Comparing and Scaling* is a unit test. The test focuses on applying the mathematical ideas from the unit and checks students' understanding of ratio, scaling, and proportion.

The Unit Project: Paper Pool

Comparing and Scaling includes an optional unit project. The project provides an opportunity for experimentation and generalization. The project is described in detail in the Assessment Resources section. A shortened version appears at the end of the student text.

Introducing Your Students to *Comparing and Scaling*

One way to introduce this unit is by discussing the three questions on the opening page of the student edition, which are designed to start students thinking about ratio and proportion. Let students express their ideas about each question. You might have them share ideas in partners and then describe their thinking.

The purpose of raising these questions is to see what students spontaneously come up with, not to teach solution strategies. This exercise should give you a good idea of how advanced they are in proportional reasoning already. After students comment, extend their thinking with questions such as these: How could you use fractions to express the data? How could you use percents to express the data?

Summarize by explaining the following: The questions we have just discussed are similar to many that occur in other situations. The unit we are starting will help you develop your skill in thinking about these kinds of comparison problems. You will see

Comparing and Scaling

Arvind and Mariah are testing four different orange juice recipes to see which tastes best. Mix A has 2 cups of orange juice concentrate and 3 cups of water; mix B has 1 cup of concentrate and 4 cups of water; mix C has 4 cups of concentrate and 8 cups of water; and mix D has 3 cups of concentrate and 5 cups of water. Which mix will taste the most "orangey"?

Madeline's car went 580 miles with 19 gallons of gas. Luis's car went 452 miles with 15.5 gallons of gas. Which car got better gas mileage?

South Dakota has a population of 721,000 and a land area of 75,896 square miles. North Dakota has a population of 638,000 and a land area of 68,994 square miles. Which of these states is more densely populated?

We use lots of different words to make comparisons—faster, stronger, taller, richer, smarter, heavier, safer, tastier, and so on. Sometimes, words alone give us all the information we need. It is enough to know that one box is heavier than another, one printer is faster than another, or one car is safer than another.

Other times, we need to know more information. We want to know, How much heavier? or How much faster? or How much safer? Answering questions like these usually involves comparing data gathered by counting, measuring, or rating things. In this unit, you will explore many different ways to make comparisons, and you will learn how to decide which comparison method is best in a given situation.

that many of the mathematical ideas and skills you are already familar with—fractions, decimals, percents, rates, and even tables, graphs, and algebraic equations—can be used to help solve problems that involve making comparisons.

Mathematical Highlights

The Mathematical Highlights page provides information for students and for parents and other family members. It gives students a preview of the activities and problems in *Comparing and Scaling*. As they work through the unit, students can refer back to the Mathematical Highlights page to review what they have learned and to preview what is still to come. This page also tells students' families what mathematical ideas and activities will be covered as the class works through *Comparing and Scaling*.

Mathematical Highlights

In *Comparing and Scaling* you will explore ways of making comparisons among quantities and ways of reasoning about quantities. The unit should help you to

- Understand and use the everyday language that asks comparison questions, such as "Which car has the best fuel economy?" and "What percent of girls play basketball?";

- Decide when the most informative comparison is the difference between two quantities, and when it is the ratio between a pair of quantities;

- Find equivalent ratios to make accurate and insightful comparisons;

- Scale a ratio up or down so that a larger or smaller object or population has the same relative characteristics as the original;

- Set up and solve proportions that arise in applications;

- Look for patterns in rate tables usable for making predictions beyond the table;

- Connect unit rates with the rule describing the situation and the constant growth in a table with a straight-line graph; and

- Solve problems which involve making comparisons and reasoning with rates, ratios and proportions.

As you work on the problems in this unit, ask yourself questions about situations that involve making comparisons and reasoning with rates, ratios and proportions: *What quantities are in the problem? How are they related? Am I being asked to make a comparison? If so, what computations will be the most useful to perform to make a comparison? Can the relationships be expressed as differences, rates, ratios, or proportions? What models or diagrams might be useful in solving the problem?*

The Investigations

The teaching materials for each investigation consist of three parts: an overview, student pages with teaching outlines, and detailed notes for teaching the investigation.

The overview of each investigation includes brief descriptions of the problems, the mathematical and problem-solving goals of the investigation, and a list of necessary materials.

Essential information for teaching the investigation is provided in the margins around the student pages. The "At a Glance" overviews are brief outlines of the Launch, Explore, and Summarize phases of each problem for reference as you work with the class. To help you assign homework, a list of "Assignment Choices" is provided next to each problem. Wherever space permits, answers to problems, follow-ups, ACE questions, and Mathematical Reflections appear next to the appropriate student pages.

The Teaching the Investigation section follows the student pages and is the heart of the Connected Mathematics curriculum. This section describes in detail the Launch, Explore, and Summarize phases for each problem. It includes all the information needed for teaching, along with suggestions for what you might say at key points in the teaching. Use this section to prepare lessons and as a guide for teaching investigations.

Assessment Resources

The Assessment Resources section contains blackline masters and answer keys for the quizzes, the check-up, the Question Bank, and the Unit Test. It also provides guidelines for assigning the optional unit project. Samples of students' work, along with a teacher's comments about how each sample was assessed, will help you to evaluate your students' efforts on the take-home project of the Unit Test. Blackline masters for the Notebook Checklist and the Self-Assessment are given. These instruments support student self-evaluation, an important aspect of assessment in the Connected Mathematics curriculum.

Blackline Masters

The Blackline Masters section includes masters for all labsheets and transparencies. Blackline masters of grid paper are also provided.

Additional Practice

Practice pages for each investigation offer additional problems for students who need more practice with the basic concepts developed in the investigations as well as some continual review of earlier concepts.

Descriptive Glossary

The Descriptive Glossary provides descriptions and examples of the key concepts in *Comparing and Scaling*. These descriptions are not intended to be formal definitions, but are meant to give you an idea of how students might make sense of these important concepts.

Making Comparisons

Throughout their previous years in school, students have made comparisons of numbers by finding the difference between them. Such comparisons only require corresponding measures from two or more situations. In many situations, however, more useful comparisons are made by using multiplication (or division) strategies rather than such addition (or subtraction) strategies. When pizza is to be shared, for example, both the number of pizzas and the number of people are factors in determining how much pizza each person will get. "Pizzas per person" is a kind of ratio called a *rate*. This kind of comparison is based on two measures, and the underlying operation is multiplication (division). This investigation introduces students to the comparison of ratios, or *proportional reasoning*.

In Problem 1.1, Writing Ads, students informally explore strategies for presenting quantitative comparison information. The language of ratios is introduced through the phrasing of comparisons that are typical of advertisements. In Problem 1.2, Targeting an Audience, students work with some simple data about student preferences as they continue their exploration of analyzing, critiquing, and forming common types of comparison statements. In Problem 1.3, Getting the Message Across, students use data from a survey of households to compare the popularity of camping among different age groups. As in many real-world comparison situations, the numbers are quite large, and students will have to discover ways to work with them.

Mathematical and Problem-Solving Goals

- *To explore several ways to make comparisons*

- *To begin to understand how to determine when comparisons can be made using multiplication or division versus addition or subtraction*

- *To begin to develop ways to use ratios, fractions, rates, and unit rates to answer questions involving proportional reasoning*

Materials		
Problem	**For students**	**For the teacher**
All	Graphing calculators	Transparencies 1.1 to 1.3 (optional)
1.1		Advertisements containing comparisons (optional)
1.3	Large sheets of paper (optional; 1 per group)	

Making Comparisons

It's easy to decide which of two numbers is larger or smaller. However, it's not as easy to decide on the best way to explain *how much* larger or smaller one number is than another—especially when one or both of the numbers are fractions. In this unit, you will learn several ways to compare numbers.

1.1 Writing Ads

In their advertisements, companies often refer to surveys to show that people prefer their product over a competitor's product. An ad for Bolda Cola starts like this:

To complete the ad, Bolda Cola wants to report the results of their taste tests. A copywriter from the advertising department has proposed four possible concluding statements.

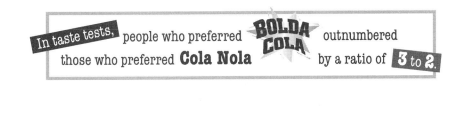

At a Glance

Grouping: small groups

Launch

- Ask the class for examples of ads and commercials that involve comparisons.

- With the class, read the Bolda Cola ad and the four concluding statements.

Explore

- Circulate as groups work on the problem and follow-up, looking for students who are having trouble analyzing the comparisons.

- Look for insights about what information each comparison does and does not give. Find ways to bring them out in the summary.

Summarize

- Make a chart summarizing the class findings about each statement.

- Ask groups to share the other statements they wrote.

Assignment Choices

ACE questions 6–11

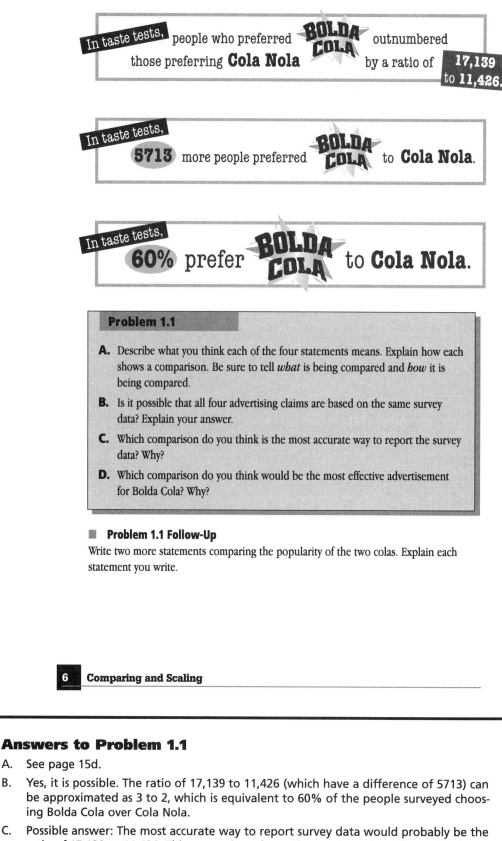

In taste tests, people who preferred **BOLDA COLA** outnumbered those preferring **Cola Nola** by a ratio of **17,139 to 11,426.**

In taste tests, **5713** more people preferred **BOLDA COLA** to **Cola Nola**.

In taste tests, **60%** prefer **BOLDA COLA** to **Cola Nola**.

Problem 1.1

A. Describe what you think each of the four statements means. Explain how each shows a comparison. Be sure to tell *what* is being compared and *how* it is being compared.

B. Is it possible that all four advertising claims are based on the same survey data? Explain your answer.

C. Which comparison do you think is the most accurate way to report the survey data? Why?

D. Which comparison do you think would be the most effective advertisement for Bolda Cola? Why?

■ Problem 1.1 Follow-Up

Write two more statements comparing the popularity of the two colas. Explain each statement you write.

Answers to Problem 1.1

A. See page 15d.

B. Yes, it is possible. The ratio of 17,139 to 11,426 (which have a difference of 5713) can be approximated as 3 to 2, which is equivalent to 60% of the people surveyed choosing Bolda Cola over Cola Nola.

C. Possible answer: The most accurate way to report survey data would probably be the ratio of 17,139 to 11,426. This comparison shows the exact number of people who were surveyed and their preferences.

D. See page 15d.

Answer to Problem 1.1 Follow-Up

See the Summarize section for a few possible statements.

1.2 Targeting an Audience

Many middle and high school students work delivering papers, mowing lawns, or baby-sitting. Students who have money of their own to spend are a common target audience for radio and television ads. Information about the amount of time students spend watching television or listening to the radio influences how companies who want to sell products to them spend their advertising dollars. Advertisers want to know which type of media will best get their message across.

Problem 1.2

A survey of 100 students at Neilson Middle School found that 60 students prefer watching television in the evening and 40 prefer listening to the radio.

A. Read the statements below about how Neilson students prefer to spend their evenings. Tell whether each statement accurately reports the results of the survey. Explain your answers.

   1. 6 out of 10 students prefer television to radio.

   2. Students prefer radio to television by a ratio of 4 to 6.

   3. Students who prefer television outnumber those who prefer radio by 20.

   4. Students who prefer television outnumber those who prefer radio by a ratio of 3 to 2.

   5. The number of students who prefer watching television is 1.5 times the number who prefer listening to radio.

   6. 40% of the students prefer radio to television.

   7. $\frac{3}{5}$ of the students prefer television to radio.

B. If you were writing a paper to convince local merchants that they would reach more students by advertising on the radio than on television, which statement from above would you use? Why?

C. Imagine that you are the advertising director for a television station in the town where Neilson is located. You have been asked to prepare a report for a meeting between your ad department and a large local skateboard manufacturer. Which accurate statement from above would you use to try to convince the manufacturer to advertise on your station? Why?

At a Glance

Grouping:
small groups

Launch

- With the class, read the information about advertisers.

Explore

- Have small groups examine the seven statements and answer the questions.

- Help groups who are struggling to understand the various comparisons.

- Listen for good ideas about the accuracy and effectiveness of the statements.

Summarize

- Talk about and resolve any disagreements about the statements.

- Ask groups to explain which statements they would use to present convincing arguments in parts B and C.

- Help the class conduct a survey about their own preferences.

Answers to Problem 1.2

A. All of the statements report the results accurately. However, statement 3 could be seriously misleading, as it does not indicate the *relative* difference—is it 1020 to 1000, or 21 to 1?

B. Possible answer: The "40% prefer radio" statement, because it presents radio in a positive way and sounds more impressive than the other statements.

C. Possible answer: The "6 out of 10" statement, because it presents television in a positive light, or the "1.5 times the number" statement, because it sounds impressive.

Assignment Choices

ACE questions 1–5, 13, and unassigned choices from earlier problems

1.3

Getting the Message Across

Launch

- Allow students to share their camping experiences.

- Review the data in the table, and pose the problem of writing a news story based on the data.

Explore

- Have pairs or small groups work on the problem.

- Help groups who are having trouble working with the large numbers.

- Ask groups to write their comparison statements on large sheets of paper. *(optional)*

Summarize

- Discuss the groups' headlines and opening sentences.

- Talk about the kinds of comparison statements students wrote.

- Review the follow-up question.

Assignment Choices

ACE questions 12, 14, and unassigned choices from earlier problems

---

▓ Problem 1.2 Follow-Up

Conduct a quick survey in your class to find out how many students prefer watching television in the evening and how many prefer listening to the radio. Record the results in a table.

1. For each statement in part A on page 7, write a similar statement about your class data.

2. In what ways is your class data similar to the Neilson data? In what ways is your data different?

3. You may have heard people talk about an interest group *manipulating* data to promote their cause. This doesn't mean they used incorrect data, but that they made careful decisions about which data to use and how to represent the data to support their cause. How could you manipulate your class data to persuade local merchants to advertise on radio rather than on television?

1.3 Getting the Message Across

Camping is a popular activity in the United States. Every year, millions of families visit national, state, and local parks to enjoy the wonders of nature. While some of these visitors "rough it" in tents, many prefer cabins, trailers, and campers—bringing a few comforts of home to the wilderness.

Answers to Problem 1.2 Follow-Up

1, 2.   Answers will depend on the class data.

3.   Look for statements that present radio in the best light.

The following table gives data on the popularity of camping for several age groups in the United States. It shows the number of people in each age group who go camping at least twice a year. The numbers in the table are projections based on data from a sample of 10,000 households.

Camping Data

	Ages 12–17	Ages 18–24	Ages 25–34
Total in the age group	21,304,000	26,650,000	41,808,000
Number who camp at least twice a year	5,336,000	4,767,000	10,000,000

Source: National Sporting Goods Association, as found in the *Statistical Abstract of the United States 1995*. Published by the Bureau of the Census, Washington, D.C., p. 260.

Problem 1.3

Suppose you were asked to write a news story about the popularity of camping in the United States based on the data in the table.

A. What headline would you use for your story? What would your first sentence be?

B. Write five statements you could use in your story to compare the popularity of camping among people in the three age groups. In each statement, be clear about which groups you are comparing. Your comparisons should be specific and based on mathematics.

Problem 1.3 Follow-Up

According to the data, what percent of people from age 12 to 34 go camping at least twice a year?

Answers to Problem 1.3

A. Headlines and sentences will vary. Students might give raw numbers rather than comparisons, such as the fact that about 20 million people from the ages of 12 to 34 go camping each year. Or, they might write headlines or sentences incorporating fractions or percents.

B. Statements will vary.

Answer to Problem 1.3 Follow-Up

The total in all age groups is 89,762,000, and the total in all age groups who camp is 20,103,000, so the percent who camp is about 22%.

Answers

Applications

1. Possible answer: Students spent more time <u>in recreation</u> than <u>watching television</u> by a ratio of <u>2</u> to <u>1</u>.

2. The number of hours spent watching television is about <u>0.79</u> times the number of hours spent doing chores or homework.

3. <u>46</u> percent of the weekend was spent <u>sleeping and eating</u>, and <u>23</u> percent of the weekend was spent <u>in recreation and watching television</u>.

As you work on these ACE questions, use your calculator whenever you need it.

Applications

In 1–4, use the following information: Oksana surveyed her class to find out how students spend their time over a weekend. On Friday, she distributed a list of activities and asked her classmates to keep track of how many hours they spent from midnight on Friday to midnight on Sunday doing each activity. On Monday, she collected the data and found the mean number of hours the students spent in each category. She put her results in a table.

Weekend Activities

Activity	Average number of hours
Sleeping	18.4 hours
Eating	3.5 hours
Recreation	7.4 hours
Talking on the phone	0.6 hours
Watching television	3.7 hours
Doing chores or homework	4.7 hours
Other	9.7 hours

In 1–3, use Oksana's data to fill in the blanks to create an accurate statement.

1. In comparing time spent watching television to recreation time, students spent more time _____ than _____ by a ratio of _____ to _____.

2. The number of hours spent watching television is about _____ times the number of hours spent doing chores or homework.

3. In comparing time spent eating and sleeping to time spent in recreation and watching television, _____ percent of the weekend was spent _____, and _____ percent was spent _____.

4. Make up a comparison like those in questions 1–3 about the data in Oksana's table. Tell why you think your comparison is interesting.

Connections

5. Below is a drawing of the spinner used in the Big Wheel game at the Waverly Middle School fun night. The chart shows the data from 236 spins of the Big Wheel.

Spin Results

Win	Lose
46	190

a. Use the data in the table to make a ratio comparison, a percent comparison, and a difference comparison.

b. Choose one of the methods of comparison from part a (ratios, percents, or differences). Think of a situation in which this method would be an effective way to report the spin results. Explain your reasoning.

c. Explain how you could find the probability of getting a win in one spin of the spinner without using the data in the chart.

d. Do the results in the table seem to agree with or contradict the probability statement you made in part c?

4. Possible answer: The ratio of eating to sleeping was 3.5 to 18.4. This is interesting, because the time spent sleeping is over 5 times the time spent eating.

Connections

5a. Possible answer: The ratio of wins to spins is 46 to 236, of losses to spins is 190 to 236, of wins to losses is 46 to 190, and of losses to wins is 190 to 46. 19% of the players were winners, 81% of the players were losers, and 62% more people lost than won. 144 more people lost than won.

5b. Possible answer: If you wanted to tell someone their chances of winning, you could say they have about a 19% chance of being a winner.

5c. Since 1 out of 5 spaces on the wheel would make you a winner, the probability of winning is 20%.

5d. The results in the table are very close to the predicted results.

6. See below right.

7. Possible answer:
$\frac{1}{3} < \frac{1}{2}$

8. Possible answer:
$\frac{5}{6} > 0.4$

9. $\frac{4}{5} < \frac{11}{12}$

10. $2.5 > 0.259$

11. $1\frac{3}{4} > 1.5$

Extensions

12a. Possible answer: In 1980, the ratio of National Forest Service area visitor hours to total federal recreation area visitor hours was 2819 million to 6367 million or about 0.44 or $\frac{4}{9}$. In 1990, this ratio was 3157 to 7567 or about 0.42 or $\frac{5}{12}$.

12b. The ratios are easier to compare than the numbers of hours. The ratio of National Forest Service visitor hours to federal recreation area visitor hours declined between 1980 and 1990 (from 44% to 42%).

---

6. Copy the number line below. Add labels for 0.25, $\frac{6}{8}$, $1\frac{3}{4}$, and 1.3.

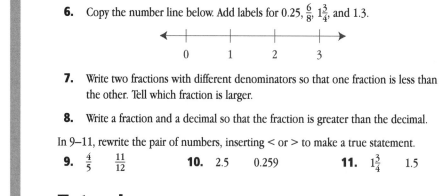

7. Write two fractions with different denominators so that one fraction is less than the other. Tell which fraction is larger.

8. Write a fraction and a decimal so that the fraction is greater than the decimal.

In 9–11, rewrite the pair of numbers, inserting < or > to make a true statement.

9. $\frac{4}{5}$ $\frac{11}{12}$ **10.** 2.5 0.259   **11.** $1\frac{3}{4}$ 1.5

Extensions

12. The first row of the table below shows the number of hours visitors spent in federal recreation areas in 1980 and 1990. Some of these federal recreation areas are managed by the National Forest Service. The second row of the table shows how many of the hours from the first row were spent in National Forest Service areas.

Hours Spent in Recreation Areas

	Visitor hours in 1980	Visitor hours in 1990
Federal recreation areas	6,367,000,000	7,567,000,000
National Forest Service areas	2,819,000,000	3,157,000,000

Source: 1980, the U.S. Heritage Conservation and Recreation Service; 1990, the U.S. National Park Service; as found in the *Statistical Abstract of the United States 1995*. Published by the Bureau of the Census, Washington, D.C., p. 251.

a. Write statements for each year, 1980 and 1990, comparing visitor hours in National Forest Service areas to visitor hours in all federal recreation areas.

b. Do the statements you wrote show visitor hours in National Forest Service areas growing or declining in comparison to visitor hours in federal recreation areas? Explain how you got your answer.

12 Comparing and Scaling

6.

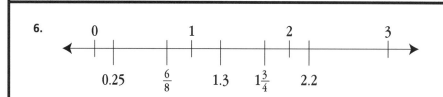

13. The table below shows the number of new books and new editions published in several subject areas in 1980 and 1990.

New Books and New Editions

Subject	Published in 1980	Published in 1990
Art	1691	1262
Education	1011	1039
Fiction	2835	5764
Juvenile	2859	5172
Literature	1686	2049
Total new books and new editions	**42,377**	**46,738**

Source: *Publishers Weekly*, as found in the *Statistical Abstract of the United States 1995*. Published by the Bureau of the Census, Washington, D.C., p. 580.

a. Compare the change in the number of new books and new editions published in 1980 and 1990 in each subject area by computing differences.

b. For 1980, find the percent of all new books and new editions that were published in each subject area.

c. For 1990, find the percent of all new books and new editions that were published in each subject area.

d. Describe how the percent of books published in each subject area changed from 1980 to 1990.

e. Which method of comparison (differences or percents) would you choose if you were a librarian making a case for an increased budget for fiction books in your library? Explain your reasoning.

f. Which method of comparison would you choose if you were a reporter writing an article about trends in the book-publishing business over time? Explain your reasoning.

13a. The differences are −429 for art, +28 for education, +2929 for fiction, +2313 for juvenile, and +363 for literature.

13b. For 1980, the percents are about 4.0% for art, 2.4% for education, 6.7% for fiction, 6.7% for juvenile, and 4.0% for literature.

13c. For 1990, the percents are about 2.7% for art, 2.2% for education, 12.3% for fiction, 11.1% for juvenile, and 4.4% for literature.

13d. From 1980 to 1990, the percents changed by −25.4% for art, +2.8% for education, +103.3% for fiction, +80.9% for juvenile, and +21.5% for literature.

13e. Possible answer: The percent comparison, because the librarian can say that the number of fiction books published from 1980 to 1990 increased by a greater percent than any other category shown, which means that public interest in fiction has probably increased.

13f. Possible answer: I would probably use both methods of comparison. The percentages are easier to compare, and the numbers could be used in a headline to catch the readers' attention.

14. Three out of four (or 75% or $\frac{3}{4}$) of dentists surveyed recommend sugarless gum to their patients who chew gum.

14. Write an advertisement that will be more effective than the one below.

Three thousand seven hundred fourteen out of four thousand nine hundred fifty-two dentists surveyed recommend sugarless gum to their patients who chew gum.

14 **Comparing and Scaling**

Mathematical Reflections

In this investigation, you explored several ways of comparing numbers. Here are five methods for making comparisons, with examples:

Ratios: In taste tests, people who preferred Bolda Cola outnumbered those who preferred Cola Nola by a ratio of 3 to 2.

Differences: Students who prefer television outnumber those who prefer radio by 20.

Fractions: $\frac{3}{5}$ of cola drinkers prefer Bolda Cola to Cola Nola.

Percents: 28% of people aged 12–17 go camping.

Scaling: The number of students who prefer watching television is 1.5 times the number who prefer listening to the radio.

These questions will help you summarize what you have learned:

1 Give another example of each type of comparison listed above.

2 What information do you get from a ratio comparison that you don't get from a difference comparison?

Think about your answers to these questions, discuss your ideas with other students and your teacher, and then write a summary of your findings in your journal.

Possible Answers

1. *Ratios:* Students who take math their freshman year in college outnumber those who don't by a ratio of 7 to 3. *Differences:* There are 7 more cats than dogs in our neighborhood. *Fractions:* $\frac{2}{7}$ of my friends jog for exercise. *Percents:* About 75% of the money I earn is from baby-sitting. *Scaling:* The number of students in the science club who have seen an eclipse is about twice the number who haven't.

2. In ratio comparisons, you get information about the relative size of two measures or counts. For example, 5 boys to 3 girls tells you that you can arrange the group of students into sets, with 5 boys and 3 girls in each set. The ratio does not give information about how large the group is; it just describes the mix of boys and girls in the group. With differences (such as, there are 5 more boys than girls), all you know is that if you pair all the girls and boys, you will have 5 boys left over. If there are 1000 girls and 1005 boys, this is a trivial difference. But if there are 6 boys and 1 girl, it is a significant difference.

Tips for the Linguistically Diverse Classroom

Original Rebus The Original Rebus technique is described in detail in *Getting to Know Connected Mathematics*. Students make a copy of the text before it is discussed. During the discussion, they generate their own rebuses for words they do not understand; the words are made comprehensible through pictures, objects, or demonstrations. Example: Under *Differences*—key phrases for which students might make rebuses are *students* (stick figures), *who prefer* (thumbs up), *television* (a television set), *outnumber* (>), *those who prefer* (stick figures), *radio* (a radio).

TEACHING THE INVESTIGATION

1.1 • Writing Ads

This problem is a review of the common language often used to make comparisons. Through their work in this problem, students will begin to consider the kinds of questions they should ask themselves as they are solving problems that involve making comparisons.

Launch

Set the stage for this problem by asking students about their experiences with advertisements.

> Can you think of any commercials or advertisements that compare one product to another or to several others? Can you think of any that involve a comparison using numbers?

You may want to bring in an ad or two that use comparisons of numbers or measures.

Display Transparency 1.1, or read with the class the Bolda Cola ad and the four possible concluding statements. Challenge students to ask themselves questions such as the following:

> What do you know from each form of comparison given?
>
> What information is lost in each form of comparison?
>
> Is each form of comparison accurate? Is each effective?

Explore

Have students work in groups of two or three on the problem and follow-up.

The issues raised in this problem will be studied in more detail further on in the unit. Even so, watch for students who are having trouble moving beyond finding differences as *the* method of comparison. You will need to pay particular attention to those students as the unit progresses.

As you move from group to group, look for particularly good explanations or insights about what each form of comparison does and does not provide. Be sure to raise these in the summary.

Summarize

As a class, discuss what the groups found as they examined the four statements. For each form of comparison, summarize on the board or a transparency what information it gives and does not give about the data. For example, the first comparison, which uses a ratio of 3 to 2, does not reveal how many people were in the taste tests, but it immediately conveys a sense of the comparison: of every 5 people in the taste tests, 3 preferred Bolda Cola. For the third statement, you may want to point out that although the difference between 17,139 and 11,426 (from the second statement) is 5713, this statement alone does not tell how many people were surveyed. If the sample included millions of people, the difference of 5713 would be insignificant. If the sample included 6000 people, this difference would be very significant. Also talk about which statements are easier to visualize.

Students may differ in their perception of which comparison would make the most effective advertisement. Whatever choices they express, press for logical explanations.

Ask groups to share some of the statements they wrote for the follow-up. There are many ways to compare the cola popularity data. Here are some comparisons students have made.

- Taylor's group used fractions: "$\frac{3}{5}$ of the people surveyed liked Bolda Cola better."

- Dede's group used a ratio: "3 out of 5 people prefer Bolda Cola to Cola Nola."

- Carmen's group used equivalent ratios: "People prefer Bolda Cola to Cola Nola in a ratio of 6 to 4, or 30 to 20."

- Matthew's group made a visual comparison: a picture of five people drinking Bolda Cola, three smiling and two with frowns.

Don't force students to use ratios, but as the class progresses through the three problems in this investigation, continue asking questions about what information each comparison raised by the class reveals about the situation.

1.2 • Targeting an Audience

This problem provides an ideal opportunity for reviewing equivalent fractions, decimals, and percents and helping students begin to think about equivalent ratios.

Launch

Introduce the problem by reading the information about advertisers with the class.

Discuss the setting for the problem. Emphasize that 100 Neilson Middle School students were surveyed about their preferences, and that seven ways of comparing the data are given in the problem. You may want to read the seven statements as a class (leaving discussion of the statements for the groups). The statements are shown on Transparency 1.2A.

Explore

When you feel the class understands the problem, have them work in groups of two or three to examine each statement for accuracy and to answer the questions.

As you circulate, look for groups who are struggling to make sense of the statements, and ask questions to help them sort out the information. Listen for good arguments about why each statement is accurate and why some are more effective than others.

Summarize

Ask groups to report on any statements that they initially disagreed about and how they resolved their disagreements. If any disagreements remain, let individuals present their arguments to help the class decide what seems reasonable.

As students explain how they concluded that each statement was accurate, you can review alternate ways of explaining equivalent ratios. For parts B and C, ask groups to explain what they chose as the best way to express the comparison of preferences and to defend their choices.

For the follow-up, groups must come together to conduct a class survey about who prefers to watch television in the evening and who prefers to listen to the radio. If some students say they prefer neither, decide as a class how to handle these data. Some classes add additional categories; others stay with just the two and ask students to express a preference (even if it's not what they actually do). Help the class summarize the data in a table, and ask each student to make a record of the class data.

Talk about the results of the survey, using the follow-up questions to continue the summary. For statements 1–7 in Problem 1.2, you could ask groups to offer their companion statements about the class data and explanations for why they think each statement is accurate. Discuss each companion statement until the class reaches a consensus.

Talk about other ways in which the class data are similar to and different from the Neilson Middle School data. Let groups share their ideas about how the class data could be manipulated to persuade local merchants to advertise on radio.

1.3 • Getting the Message Across

In this problem, students use data from a table to compare interest in camping by people of various ages. Because the totals in the three age groups differ, students cannot simply compare the numbers of campers. Fraction or rate comparisons are necessary to make accurate statements.

Launch

You may want to initiate a class discussion about camping to introduce the topic. Perhaps take a quick survey of how many students have been camping, where they went, who they went with, and what kind of shelter they used. Then, pose the idea of writing a news story based on the data in the table.

Decide whether you want groups to record their results (in large print) on large sheets of paper, which can be displayed during the summary. This way, additional time for recording the statements on the board will not be needed.

Explore

Have students work on the problem in pairs or small groups.

The numbers in the table are very large; students will either need to round them to make simple ratio or fraction comparisons, or use calculators to obtain decimals or percents. If groups are having trouble because of the size of the numbers, ask questions to help them think about the fact that the three final zeros do not affect ratio comparisons, and that the numbers can be rounded to produce friendlier ratios. For example, for the 12–17 age group, we could say that the ratio between the whole group and those who go camping is about 20 to 5 (or 4 to 1), or that about 25% of this group goes camping.

Summarize

Bring the class together, and ask groups to share their headlines and first sentences. Ask clarifying questions about their meanings. Then, collect the comparison statements that the groups wrote by displaying the large sheets of paper or by having each group write their comparisons on a section of the board. As each group explains their work, help the class examine the statements for accuracy and for effectiveness in making a comparison.

Many statements can be made to compare the popularity of camping among the three age groups. For example, students may use ratios, such as comparing the ratio of people in the 12–17 age group who go camping to the total in the age group (5336 to 21,304) to the ratio of those who do not go camping (15,968 to 21,304). For this kind of information, however, fractions or percentages of a whole seem more likely choices for the comparisons of interest. For example, 25% of people in the 12–17 age group, 18% in the 18–24 age group, and 24% in the 25–34 age group go camping. Extend and assess students' thinking about the data by further questioning them about comparisons that can be made.

> Would it make sense to write that the number of campers in the 25–34 age group is about double the number in the 12–17 age group? How about in the 18–24 age group?

> Would it make sense to write that the number of campers in the 25–34 age group is about 5000 more than the number in the 18–24 age group?

Discuss the follow-up, which foreshadows the topic of the next investigation. Because students have studied percents in depth in grade 6, they may have already employed them to make comparisons in the data. However, they have probably not looked at the overall percent of the *whole group* of people who camp, which requires finding the total of all three age groups and the total who go camping. If students have calculated percents for each of the age groups, ask them to compare them to the percent for the entire group.

Additional Answers

Answers to Problem 1.1

A. The first statement means that for every 3 people who preferred Bolda Cola, 2 preferred Cola Nola. The number of people preferring each brand is being compared. The second statement is comparing the actual number of people who preferred each brand. A group of 17,139 people preferred Bolda Cola, and a group of 11,426 people preferred Cola Nola. The third statement reports the difference in numbers between the two groups of people. We can't tell how many people were surveyed, but we do know that 5713 more people preferred Bolda Cola. The last statement tells us that of the whole group surveyed, 60% preferred Bolda Cola. This means that for every 100 people surveyed, 60 liked Bolda Cola better.

D. Possible answers: The ratio 3 to 2 or the 60% might be the most effective advertisements, because the numbers are smaller and easier to relate to—you can easily use the ratio of 3 to 2 to predict what you would expect preferences to be in your class or in some other group of people. Or, the larger numbers may make a more powerful impression: the difference between 3 and 2 is only 1, while the difference between 17,139 and 11,426 is 5713.

Comparing by Finding Percents

This investigation continues the exploration of making comparisons, with an emphasis on using percents.

In Problem 2.1, Comparing Leisure Activities, students will work with real data from a survey about participation in several sports activities. There are two basic ways to work with the large numbers in the data: either use division to find decimal or percent rates, or round the data to numbers that can easily be changed to simple, whole-number ratios. This investigation encourages the use of the first method, which is easy to implement with a calculator. Throughout the investigation, however, talk with students about other ways of comparing, since rounded, whole-number ratios are generally easier to interpret and offer practice with estimation. In Problem 2.2, Comparing Your Class to the Nation, students analyze the sports activity data they collected about their own class and to make comparisons between their class data and the survey data from the previous problem.

Mathematical and Problem-Solving Goals

- **To further develop the ability to make sensible comparisons of data using ratios, fractions, and decimal rates, with a focus on percents**

- **To develop the ability to make judgments about rounding data to estimate ratio comparisons**

- **To observe what is common about situations that call for a certain type of ratio comparison**

Materials		
Problem	**For students**	**For the teacher**
All	Graphing calculators	Transparencies 2.1 and 2.2 (optional)
ACE	Centimeter grid paper (optional)	

Student Pages 16–25   Teaching the Investigation 25a–25d

Comparing by Finding Percents

What do you like to do during your free time? Do you enjoy exercising or playing sports? A 1991 survey found that the five most popular sports activities in the United States are bicycle riding, camping, exercise walking, fishing, and swimming.

Think about this!

With your class, discuss the kinds of sports activities you like to participate in. Identify four or five activities that are different from those mentioned in the national survey. List these activities, along with the activities found in the national survey, on the board. Then, survey the class, asking each student which activities he or she participates in more than once a year. Tally the results for boys and girls separately. Save the data so that you can compare your class with the national survey in a later problem.

The problems in this investigation ask you to make comparisons about data. In particular, you are asked to think about ways to use percents to make comparisons.

Remember that percent means "out of 100." You can find a percent by first dividing to find a decimal. For example, the table below shows the number of males in the United States and the number of them who swim. To find the percent of males who swim, first divide the number of male swimmers by the total number of males to get a decimal. Then, round the decimal to the nearest hundredth and change the decimal to a percent.

Males in the U.S.	111,851,000
Males who swim	27,713,000

For this data, $27,713,000 \div 111,851,000 = 0.24776711$, which rounded to the nearest hundredth is 0.25. The decimal 0.25 is equivalent to 25%, so about 25% of males swim.

2.1 Comparing Leisure Activities

The table below gives data about participation in the five most popular sports activities in the United States—bicycle riding, camping, exercise walking, fishing, and swimming. The numbers are projections based on a 1993 survey of 10,000 households. The survey counted anyone 7 years old or older who participated in an activity more than once per year. Some people participated in more than one activity. The numbers in the "Total in group" row are the total number of people in the United States population in each group.

Participation in Sports Activities

Activity	Males	Females	Ages 12–17	Ages 55–64
Bicycle riding	24,562,000	23,357,000	8,794,000	2,030,000
Camping	23,165,000	19,533,000	5,336,000	2,355,000
Exercise walking	21,054,000	43,373,000	2,816,000	7,782,000
Fishing	30,449,000	14,885,000	4,945,000	3,156,000
Swimming	27,713,000	33,640,000	10,874,000	2,756,000
Total in group	**111,851,000**	**118,555,000**	**21,304,000**	**20,922,000**

Source: National Sporting Goods Association, as found in the *Statistical Abstract of the United States 1995.* Published by the Bureau of the Census, Washington, D.C., p. 260.

Problem 2.1

In the table above, look for interesting patterns in the data for males and females and in the data for the two age groups.

A. Why don't the numbers in the columns add to the given totals?

B. Write three statements that use percents to make comparisons about the numbers of male and female participants in the various activities. Explain how you found the percents.

C. Write three statements that use percents to make comparisons about the numbers of teenage and older-adult participants in the various activities.

D. Write three statements that make comparisons about the data without using percents.

At a Glance

Grouping: pairs or small groups

Launch

- Help the class conduct a survey of the sports activities in which they participate.

- Review the data from the national survey on sports activity participation.

Explore

- As groups explore the problem, help those who are having difficulty working with the large numbers.

Summarize

- Ask groups to share their comparison statements.

- Discuss statements that convey information particularly well.

- Explore and talk about the follow-up questions.

Assignment Choices

ACE questions 1–8, 17–22 (17 requires centimeter grid paper), and unassigned choices from earlier problems

---

Answers to Problem 2.1

A. The number of people participating in each activity in each group do not add to the totals because the totals are *not* the total number of participants; they are the total number of people in the United States in that group. In fact, because some people participate in more than one activity, the total of the numbers in some columns is actually greater than the total number of people in that group.

B. Possible answer: About 22.0% of males in the United States ride bicycles. The percent of females in the United States who exercise walk (36.6%) is about twice the percent of males who exercise walk (18.8%). The percent of males in the United States who fish (27.2%) is more than twice the percent of females who fish (12.6%).

C. See page 25c.

D. See page 25c.

Comparing Your Class to the Nation

Grouping:
pairs or small groups

Launch

- Ask students to predict how the class data might compare to the national survey data.

Explore

- Have pairs or groups analyze the class data and write comparison statements.

- As groups work, look for insightful comparisons.

- Have students work on the follow-up individually, then reach consensus in groups.

Summarize

- Have groups share their comparison statements about the class data.

- Talk about the comparisons of the class data to the national data.

- Discuss the follow-up.

Assignment Choices

ACE questions 9–16 (9–15 use the class data from Problem 2.1), 23–26, and unassigned choices from earlier problems

Assessment

It is appropriate to use Check-Up 1 after this problem.

■ **Problem 2.1 Follow-Up**

1. Explain how you might decide when percents would be a good way to make a comparison and when other forms of comparison would be better. Use examples if they help explain your ideas.

2. Can you compare the participation of teenage boys in these activities to the participation of older-adult women by using the data in the table? Explain.

2.2 Comparing Your Class to the Nation

Statistics that are based on data from a small group of people, or from people who live in a particular area, may be quite different from statistics based on a national survey. For example, if there is a lake or another body of water in your area, fishing may be more popular in your class than in the nation as a whole.

In this problem, you will compare your class data with the data from the national survey. When the total numbers in two data sets are very different, representing the data values as percents of a total is a useful way to compare the data sets. Finding percents is a way of creating a common scale for two data sets by expressing all the data values as numbers "out of 100."

Did you know?

Here are some interesting percents:

- About 71% of the earth is covered by water.
- Females make up about 51.3% of the population of the United States.
- About 99% of all homes in the United States have at least one TV set, about 66% have at least two TV sets, and 65% get cable television.
- Of all the computers in the world, about 43% are in use in the United States, 22% in Europe, and 7% in Japan.
- More than 70% of the waste produced in the United States ends up in landfills.

Source: *1996 Information Please Almanac.* Ed. Otto Johnson. New York: Houghton Mifflin, 1995.

Answers to Problem 2.1 Follow-Up

1. Possible answer: Percents are a good form of comparison when we want to compare a part to a whole. If we wanted to compare males to the total number of students in a class, we could say, for example, that 75% of the class is male. When we are not comparing a part to a whole—as when we are comparing males to females—percents are harder to interpret. If a class has 7 females and 21 males, the ratio 7 to 21 compares a part to a part. An equivalent ratio is 1 to 3. This says that for every female, there are 3 males.

2. no; The data do not break down the numbers of males and females participating in each activity by age.

Problem 2.2

You conducted a class survey at the beginning of this investigation. Now, organize the results for bicycle riding, camping, exercise walking, fishing, and swimming into a table similar to the one on page 17. Your table should have separate columns for males and females.

A. Look back at the three statements you wrote in part B of Problem 2.1 comparing the numbers of male and female participants in the various activities. Now, make the same comparisons for boys and girls in your class.

B. Compare the statements about your class data to the statements about the national data.

C. Write three statements comparing sports activities of all students in your class to those of

    1. 12 to 17 year olds in the national survey

    2. 55 to 64 year olds in the national survey

■ Problem 2.2 Follow-Up

1. Write a paragraph telling how your class data is like the national data and how it is different. For any ways in which your class data appears to be different from the national data, give reasons why you think your class is different.

2. In your class survey, you added several activities to the five listed in the national survey. Write at least three statements comparing the numbers of boys and girls in your class who participate in these activities.

Answers to Problem 2.2

Answers will depend on the class data.

Answers to Problem 2.2 Follow-Up

Answers will depend on the class data.

Tips for the Linguistically Diverse Classroom

Visual Enhancement The Visual Enhancement technique is described in detail in *Getting to Know Connected Mathematics*. It involves using real objects or pictures to make information more comprehensible. Example: While discussing the information presented in the "Did you know?" feature on page 18, you might show pictures of oceans, televisions, computers, a map showing the named countries, and landfills.

Answers

Applications

1. $\frac{17}{32}$

2. $\frac{17}{32}$ = 0.53125 or about 53%

3. about 47%

4. Possible answer: Females are more likely to play basketball than football by a ratio of 14 to 4, or 7 to 2. Males are almost as likely to play football as basketball.

5. Basketball has the greatest participation, with 27 out of the 32 students, or about 84%, participating.

6. Both basketball and track and field have 13 out of 15 boys participating, which is about 87% of the boys.

7. Only softball, in which about 59% of the girls but only 53% of the boys participate

8. About 59% of the girls in the class play softball, so about 0.59 × 368 = 217 girls in the school would play softball.

As you work on these ACE questions, use your calculator whenever you need it.

Applications

In 1–8, use the following information: A homeroom class of 32 eighth graders at Springbrook Middle School completed a survey about their participation in team sports. Each student was asked to list any sport he or she liked to play. The results for four of the most popular sports are given in this table.

Participation in Team Sports

Sport	Female	Male
Basketball	14	13
Track and field	7	13
Softball	10	8
Football	4	11
Total surveyed	**17**	**15**

1. What fraction of the class is female?

2. What percent of the class is female?

3. What percent of the class is male?

4. Write two statements comparing participation in basketball to participation in football.

5. In which sport does the greatest percent of the class participate?

6. In which sport does the greatest percent of the male students participate? Explain your answer.

7. In which sports is there a greater percent of female participation than male participation? Explain your answer.

8. If the percents of participation in these sports for all students at Springbrook are approximately the same as the percents for this class, about how many of the 368 female students in the school like to play softball?

In 9–15, use the table below, which shows the national data on exercise walking.

Participation in Exercise Walking

Activity	Males	Females	Ages 12–17	Ages 55–64
Exercise walking	21,054,000	43,373,000	2,816,000	7,782,000
Total in group	**111,851,000**	**118,555,000**	**21,304,000**	**20,922,000**

Source: National Sporting Goods Association, as found in the *Statistical Abstract of the United States 1995.* Published by the Bureau of the Census, Washington, D.C., p. 260.

9. What percent of the 55–64 age group walks for exercise?

10. What percent of the 12–17 age group walks for exercise?

11. What percent of males walks for exercise?

12. Write a statement comparing the number of males who walk for exercise to the number of females who walk for exercise.

13. Write a statement comparing the number of 12 to 17 year olds who walk for exercise to the number of 55 to 64 year olds who walk for exercise.

14. Look back at your class data. Describe how your class data on exercise walking is similar to the national data and how it is different.

15. Suppose your class data reflected the same percents as the national data. How many males and females in your class would exercise walk?

9. $\frac{7782}{20,922} = 0.372$ or about 37.2%

10. $\frac{2816}{21,304} = 0.132$ or about 13.2%

11. $\frac{21,054}{111,851} = 0.188$ or about 18.8%

12. Possible answers: Females outnumber males in exercise walking by a ratio of about 43 to 21, or 2 to 1. Nearly twice as many females walk for exercise as do males. About 36.6% of females walk for exercise, compared to 18.8% of males.

13. Possible answers: About 37.2% of older people walk for exercise, while 13.2% of younger people do. Older people are more likely to walk for exercise than younger people by a ratio of about 3 to 1.

14. Answers will vary.

15. The percentages are 18.8% for males and 36.6% for females in the national data. Students should multiply the related decimals (0.188 and 0.366) by the number of males and females in the class.

Connections

16a. yes; They are similar, because $\frac{9}{12} = \frac{12}{16} = \frac{3}{4}$.

16b. The area of the large room is $12 \times 16 = 192$ ft². The area of the small room is $9 \times 12 = 108$ ft².

16c. The small room has 108 ft² for its occupant. The large room has $\frac{192}{2} = 86$ ft² for each occupant. However, if you look at *who has the most space to walk around in,* the answer is the larger room, because it has more open space and each person has access to the other's open space.

17a, b. See page 25d.

17c. The triangles are similar.

17d. The area of the small triangle is 25% of the area of the large triangle.

17e. The area of the large triangle is 400% of the area of the small triangle.

Connections

16. Below are floor plans for two college dorm rooms. One is for two students, and the other is for one student.

   a. Are the floors of the two rooms similar rectangles? Explain.

   b. For each room, what is the floor area?

   c. Which room gives each student the most space?

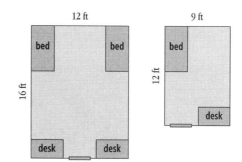

17. a. Plot the points (8, 6), (8, 22), and (24, 14) on grid paper. Connect them to form a triangle.

   b. Draw the triangle you get when you apply the rule (0.5*x*, 0.5*y*) to the three points from part a.

   c. How are the triangles from parts a and b related?

   d. The area of the smaller triangle is what percent of the area of the larger triangle?

   e. The area of the larger triangle is what percent of the area of the smaller triangle?

18. In a–f, rewrite the sentence, replacing the question mark with a number that makes the sentence true.

    a. $\frac{3}{4} < \frac{?}{12}$

    b. $\frac{3}{4} = \frac{?}{12}$

    c. $\frac{3}{4} > \frac{?}{12}$

    d. $\frac{5}{9} < \frac{?}{15}$

    e. $\frac{5}{9} = \frac{?}{15}$

    f. $\frac{5}{9} > \frac{?}{15}$

    g. Explain your strategies for solving these problems.

19. Write two fractions with different denominators and a sum of $\frac{4}{5}$.

20. Write two decimal numbers with three or fewer digits each and a sum of 12.36.

21. Write a decimal number and a fraction with a sum of 0.593.

22. A store is having a 30% off sale. How would you determine an item's sale price?

Extensions

In 23 and 24, look at the table of data about participation in sports activities on page 17.

23. Which sports activity has the greatest percent of participation by females? Which has the greatest percent of participation by males?

24. Which sports activity is most popular among the 12–17 age group? Explain.

25. Kent's department store is having a Super Saturday Sale during which every item is 25% off. When you walk in the door, a salesperson hands you a coupon for an additional 10% off the reduced price of any item. Your friend says, "Wow—if you buy something with your coupon, you will get 35% off the original price!" Is your friend correct? Why or why not?

18a. ? = any number greater than 9

18b. ? = 9

18c. ? = any number less than 9

18d. ? = any number greater than $8\frac{1}{3}$

18e. ? = $8\frac{1}{3}$

18f. ? = any number less than $8\frac{1}{3}$

18g. Strategies will vary. Possible answer: I found a common denominator, determined what number would make the fractions equal, and (in parts a, c, d, and f) then chose a number less or greater than that number.

19. Possible answer: $\frac{1}{2} + \frac{3}{10} = \frac{4}{5}$

20. Possible answer: 9.00 + 3.36 = 12.36

21. Possible answer: $0.093 + \frac{1}{2} = 0.593$

22. Possible answer: Multiply the price of the item by 0.7.

Extensions

23. Exercise walking has the greatest percent of participation by females. Fishing has the greatest percent of participation by males.

24. swimming; 51% of people ages 12–17 swim.

25. Possible answer: No, because the 10% off is applied after the 25% off is applied. If an item was originally marked $10, the store will first reduce it to $0.75 \times 10 = \$7.50$ and then to $\$7.50 \times 0.90 = \$6.75$, which is a savings of $3.25, or the same as getting a 32.5% discount.

26. Possible answer: No, because $20 × 0.90 × 0.75 is the same as $20 × 0.75 × 0.90, or $13.50.

26. At Kent's department store (from question 25), you decide to buy a T-shirt with an original price of $20. The sales clerk first uses your coupon to reduce the original price by 10% and then applies the 25% discount. Did you save more than you would have if the clerk had applied the 25% discount first and then used the 10% off coupon? Explain your answer.

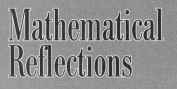

Mathematical Reflections

In this investigation, you used percents to make comparisons. You compared data for males and females and for teenagers and older adults. You developed your skill in making comparisons and in deciding what kinds of comparisons make sense. These questions will help you summarize what you have learned:

1. Give an example of a situation in which it makes sense to use percents to make comparisons.

2. Using your example from part 1, show how to make a comparison using percents.

3. Explain why percents are useful for making comparisons.

4. Give an example of a situation in which you think another form of comparison is better than percents. Explain your reasoning.

5. Can you find a percent comparison from a ratio comparison? Explain how, or tell what additional information you would need.

Think about your answers to these questions, discuss your ideas with other students and your teacher, and then write a summary of your findings in your journal.

1. Percents are a good method of comparing when you are comparing a part to a whole. If you have 5 cheese pizzas and 9 pepperoni pizzas and want to make a statement of comparison about the number of cheese pizzas you have, you could use percents.

2. You can make a comparison using percents by first forming a fraction with the number in which you are interested in the numerator and the total number in the denominator. In this case, the fraction $\frac{5}{14}$ represents the number of pizzas that are cheese. Then, you divide to get a decimal, round the decimal, and form the percent. In this case, you could round 0.357142857 to 0.36 and write it as 36%, which means that about 36% of the pizzas are cheese pizzas.

3. Percents are useful because they are easy to think about and to visualize. For example, 36% means that for every 100 things, 36 are in the special category. They are also useful because they relate to our place value system and to our money system of dollars and cents.

4. See left.

5. Yes, you can. For example, if 3 out of 4 students like chocolate, that means that if there were 100 students, about 75 out of the 100 would like chocolate, which is 75%.

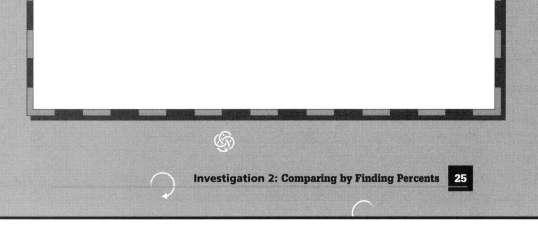

4. If you are interested in comparing the number of cheese pizzas to the number of pepperoni pizzas, percents might be hard to interpret; a ratio statement might be better. For example, the ratio of cheese pizzas to pepperoni pizzas is 5 to 9. Or, you could say that there is $\frac{5}{9}$ (or a little over half) of a cheese pizza for each pepperoni pizza.

Tips for the Linguistically Diverse Classroom

Diagram Code The Diagram Code technique is described in detail in *Getting to Know Connected Mathematics*. Students use a minimal number of words and drawings, diagrams, or symbols to respond to questions that require writing. Example: Question 3—A student might answer this question by writing % *is like* and drawing coins and dollar bills. The student might write *25% = 0.25*. The student might also show two hundred grids, one shaded 30% and one 80%, and label them *30% < 80%*.

TEACHING THE INVESTIGATION

2.1 • Comparing Leisure Activities

Begin the investigation by initiating the "Think about this!" discussion of the sports activities in which students in class participate. Get a sense of which activities seem most popular in the class. Then, when you summarize, you can refer to these earlier ideas.

Launch

Help the class make a list of the top four or five activities in the class, plus the five given in the national survey. Use the list to survey the class by asking, for each activity on the list, how many students participate in that activity more than once a year. Help the class organize the data into a table, keeping data for males and females separate. Then, ask for some conjectures about how the class compares to the nation in their sports participation.

> Which activities do you think would be most popular in national surveys of different age groups?
>
> What differences might you expect to see between males and females in a national survey?

Introduce the class to the national survey about participation in the five most popular sports activities in the United States. Ask questions about the data shown in the table.

> Do you think the numbers given are exact, or have they been rounded? *(The numbers have been rounded to thousands.)*
>
> Describe one thing that the table gives you information about.
>
> What is something you cannot tell from the data in the table?

Make sure students understand what the numbers in the "Total in group" row mean: these are estimates of the total number of people in the United States in each group. You may want to review the example on page 16 of the student edition, which shows how to find the percent of males in the United States who swim.

Read over the questions in Problem 2.1 with the class.

Explore

Have students explore the problem in pairs or small groups. If you have not reviewed finding percents with large numbers, watch carefully to see whether some groups need help. If so, ask questions to help them realize that they can choose to work with the numbers without the last three zeros; the percents will be the same. (In difference comparisons, however, the 1000s factor is quite relevant.)

Summarize

Ask groups to share their comparison statements with the class. Lots of interesting comparisons can be made from these data. For example, bicycle riding is more than four times as popular among teens than among older adults, camping is about twice as popular, and swimming is about four times as popular. Only exercise walking is more popular among older adults than teens, by a ratio of about 3 to 1.

For the Teacher: Data for Problem 2.1

In making comparisons between the data for teenagers and for adults, it is worth noting that the indicated age spans are different—6 years for teens and 10 years for adults. However, the population totals are very close in each age span, so the numbers can be compared directly.

Allow the class to discuss whether they think each statement is accurate, and encourage comments on statements that seem particularly effective at conveying information.

Use the follow-up questions as part of the summary. Ask students to jot down their thoughts on how to recognize when percents would be a good form of comparison.

> Think of a situation in which percents would be appropriate and another situation in which some other form of comparison makes more sense.

When everyone has had a few minutes to think, let students share their ideas. Have the class identify examples and explanations that they think are very helpful in showing when certain kinds of comparisons are useful.

2.2 • Comparing Your Class to the Nation

This investigation provides opportunities for students to make quantitative comparisons. The data require careful reading and thoughtful interpretation.

Launch

Read through the introduction to the problem with the class. Ask them to predict ways in which the class data might be similar to and different from the national survey data they have just analyzed.

Explore

Have students work in pairs or groups to analyze the class data and to write comparison statements. As groups work, look for particularly good insights into similarities and differences between the class data and the national survey data, and make sure these are shared during the summary. Remind students to supply data to support their observations.

For the follow-up, ask each student to write an individual response and then share their answers in their group to reach consensus about what to report to the class in the summary.

Summarize

Have groups share some of their statements about the class data. Then, discuss the groups' comparisons of the class data to the national data.

For the Teacher: Importance of Context

One of the most important messages from this summary and this unit should be that the context of the data must be revisited to determine whether statements about the data make sense. There are no easy algorithms for deciding when to choose certain kinds of comparisons; the context drives which mathematical representations are used. Students must have opportunities to talk through many problems to begin to see the kinds of questions they need to ask themselves in order to check their statements against a problem's original context.

Try to help students understand that every time they form a ratio of two numbers in fraction form, there is an indicated division. When the division is performed and a decimal answer is produced, the decimal must be interpreted with labels so that the number has meaning. For example, if we say "the percent of boys who swim is _____," we are labeling the percent as having come from a division of the number of boys who swim by the total number of boys in the group.

When the class discusses the follow-up, ask questions about local conditions that might be responsible for some of the differences between the class data and the national survey data. For example, students who live near national or state parks probably camp and fish more than students who live in metropolitan areas. Students who live in colder climates with no access to a heated swimming pool probably do not swim as much as do students in warmer climates or with access to swimming facilities. A local culture may support a particular kind of activity; in some areas, for example, organized bike tours are popular.

Additional Answers

Answers to Problem 2.1

C. Possible answer: Among the 12–17 year olds, 41.2% ride bicycles, but among the older group only 9.7% are bicycle riders. The percent of 12 to 17 year olds who swim is about 51.0%, or about half of the people in this age group in the United States. About 37.2% of people age 55 to 64 exercise walk.

D. Possible answer: The ratio of 12 to 17 year olds to 55 to 64 year olds who swim is about 4 to 1. More females than males exercise walk; they outnumber males by a ratio of about 43 to 21, or about 2 to 1. Males who fish outnumber females who fish by a ratio of about 2 to 1.

ACE Answers

Connections

17a, b.

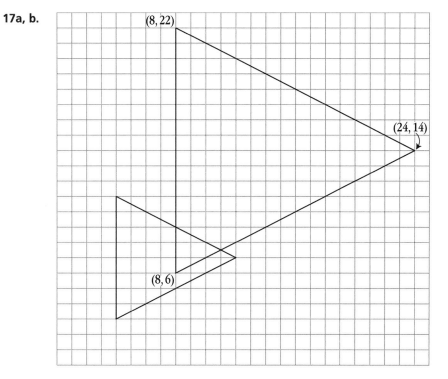

Comparing by Using Ratios

Once ratios, fractions, decimals, or percents have been used to describe relationships among quantitative measures, the next step is usually to make things larger or smaller while maintaining those relationships. This is the process involved in making scale models, building life-size objects from scale models, and extrapolating from recipes proportionally. In this investigation, students begin to develop strategies for scaling ratios to make comparisons or to find missing parts of equivalent ratios.

Problem 3.1, Mixing Juice, helps students focus on the part-to-whole meaning of fractions. Students informally explore rates and ratios, using proportional reasoning to determine how to combine orange juice concentrate and water to make enough orange juice for a given number of people. They are encouraged to use several strategies, including forming ratios, to solve the proportion problems. In Problem 3.2, Helping the Cook, students consider a typical recipe scaling problem, determining how many cans of tomatoes are needed to make spaghetti sauce for a given number of people based on a recipe for a smaller batch. Problem 3.3, Sharing Pizza, involves a comparison between two table sizes and two amounts of pizza. Students are challenged to determine whether the two arrangements allocate pizza to people in a fair way.

Mathematical and Problem-Solving Goals

- **To recognize situations in which ratios are a useful form of comparison**

- **To form, label, and interpret ratios from numbers given or implied in a situation**

- **To explore several informal strategies for solving scaling problems involving ratios (which is equivalent to solving proportions)**

Materials		
Problem	**For students**	**For the teacher**
All	Graphing calculators, centimeter grid paper (optional)	Transparencies 3.1 to 3.3 (optional)
3.1	Orange and white chips or squares of paper (optional; about 25 orange and 100 white per group)	Can of orange juice concentrate and pitcher (optional)

Comparing by Using Ratios

Another useful way to compare numbers is to form *ratios*. You looked at ratios informally in Investigation 1. In this investigation, you will learn to form and interpret ratios in order to make comparisons. Let's look at some examples of statements containing ratios.

In taste tests, people who preferred Bolda Cola outnumbered those who preferred Cola Nola by a ratio of 3 to 2.

The ratio of boys to girls in our class is 12 boys to 15 girls.

The ratio of boys to students in our class is 12 boys to 27 students.

The ratio of kittens to cats in our neighborhood is $\frac{1}{4}$.

The sign in the hotel lobby says 1 dollar Canadian: 0.85 dollars U.S.

A paint mixture calls for 5 parts blue paint to 2 parts yellow paint.

In these examples, ratios are written in three different ways: using the word "to," as in 5 to 8, using the ":" symbol, as in 5:8, and using fraction notation, as in $\frac{5}{8}$. All three forms—5 to 8, 5:8, and $\frac{5}{8}$—mean that for every five of the first item, there are eight of the second item.

Think about this!

Look over the examples above. Think about what is being compared in each ratio.

- Is the ratio comparing two parts of the same whole? This is called a *part-to-part* ratio.
- Is the ratio comparing a part of a whole to the whole? This is called a *part-to-whole* ratio.
- Is the ratio comparing two different kinds of things?

Many real-world problems involve scaling a ratio up or down to find an *equivalent ratio*. This requires finding larger or smaller numbers with the same relationship as the numbers in the original ratio. For example, the ratios 2:3, 4:6, and 6:9 are all equivalent. Suppose a shade of purple paint is made using 2 parts red paint to 3 parts blue. You would get the same shade of purple whether you mixed 2 gallons of red paint to 3 gallons of blue paint, 4 gallons of red paint to 6 gallons of blue paint, or 6 gallons of red paint to 9 gallons of blue paint.

3.1 Mixing Juice

Every year, the seventh grade students at Langston Hughes School go on an outdoor-education camping trip. During the week-long trip, the students study nature and participate in recreational activities. Everyone pitches in to help with the cooking and cleanup.

Arvind and Mariah are in charge of making orange juice for all the campers. They make the juice by mixing water and orange juice concentrate. To find the mix that tastes best, Arvind and Mariah decided to test some recipes on a few of their friends.

Tips for the Linguistically Diverse Classroom

Enactment The Enactment technique is described in detail in *Getting to Know Connected Mathematics*. Students act out mini-scenes, using props, to make information comprehensible. Example: While discussing Problem 3.1, show the outdoor setting by sharing pictures of campgrounds or the forest. Assign students to play Arvind and Mariah, and have them model making orange juice from a can of concentrate.

- - - - - - - - -
At a Glance

Grouping: small groups

Launch

- As a class, review the ratio comparison statements and the scaling example.
- Introduce the topic of making juice from concentrate.

Explore

- As groups work on parts A and B, assist those who are having trouble.
- If needed, bring groups together for a summary of parts A and B before they explore part C.

Summarize

- Explore the methods students have discovered for the three parts of the problem.
- Let students build models to represent the ratio of concentrate to water in one of the mixes. *(optional)*
- Discuss the follow-up.

Assignment Choices

ACE questions 1, 2, 9–12, and unassigned choices from earlier problems

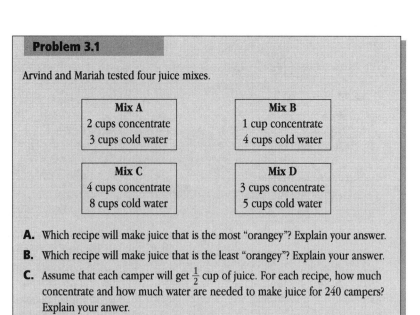

Problem 3.1

Arvind and Mariah tested four juice mixes.

Mix A
2 cups concentrate
3 cups cold water

Mix B
1 cup concentrate
4 cups cold water

Mix C
4 cups concentrate
8 cups cold water

Mix D
3 cups concentrate
5 cups cold water

A. Which recipe will make juice that is the most "orangey"? Explain your answer.

B. Which recipe will make juice that is the least "orangey"? Explain your answer.

C. Assume that each camper will get $\frac{1}{2}$ cup of juice. For each recipe, how much concentrate and how much water are needed to make juice for 240 campers? Explain your anwer.

■ **Problem 3.1 Follow-Up**

1. How did you use ratios in solving Problem 3.1?

2. For each recipe, how much concentrate and how much water is needed to make 1 cup of juice?

Did you know?

Here are some interesting ratios:

- There are about 21 white vans on the road for every purple van.
- In 1994, about 493 music CDs were sold for every 10 albums sold.
- For the first 60 miles of depth, the temperature of the earth increases 1°F for every 100–200 feet.
- The ratio of people 5 to 17 years old in the United States to people 85 years of age or older is about 15 to 1.
- Cigarette smoking accounts for 3 out of 10 deaths due to cancer.

Source: *World Almanac and Book of Facts 1996.* Ed. Robert Famighetti. Mahwa, New Jersey: Funk and Wagnalls, 1995.

Answers to Problem 3.1

A.   Mix A will make the most orangey juice. (See possible explanations in the Summarize section.)

B.   Mix B will make the least orangey juice.

C.   See page 36f.

Answers to Problem 3.1 Follow-Up

1.   Answers will vary, but every group should be able to point out how they used ratios of concentrate to water or ratios of concentrate to total juice.

2.   See page 36f.

The camp cook must buy enough ingredients for all the meals he intends to prepare during the week. One of the cook's most popular meals is spaghetti. The spaghetti recipe he uses calls for canned tomatoes. The CannedStuff store has large cans of tomatoes on sale, five cans for $4.00. The cook says he can make sauce for five to six campers from each can of tomatoes.

Problem 3.2

Suppose you are assigned to help the cook order supplies.

A. How many cans of tomatoes would you advise the cook to buy to make spaghetti for the 240 campers? Explain your answer.

B. How much would these cans of tomatoes cost altogether?

■ Problem 3.2 Follow-Up

1. At the EatMore grocery store, you can buy seven cans of tomatoes for $6.00. The cans are the same size as the cans at CannedStuff. Are the tomatoes at EatMore a better buy than the tomatoes at CannedStuff? Explain your answer.

2. Gus was trying to figure out how to think about the EatMore price of seven cans of tomatoes for $6.00. He divided 7 by 6 and got 1.16666667. He then divided 6 by 7 and got 0.85714286. What does each of these numbers mean in the context of seven cans of tomatoes for $6.00?

At a Glance

Grouping: small groups

Launch

■ Introduce the problem, and make sure students understand the questions.

Explore

■ As groups work, you can make an informal assessment of how well students are understanding ratios.

■ If groups finish early, ask them to find other ways to think about the problem.

Summarize

■ Discuss the variety of ways groups reasoned about each question in the problem and follow-up.

Answers to Problem 3.2

A. Possible answer: You want to make sure you have enough tomato sauce on hand. Based on the upper and lower estimates of people served per can of tomatoes, the cook will need between 240 ÷ 5 = 48 and 240 ÷ 6 = 40 cans. (Some students may say that the cook must buy at least 48 cans to guarantee there will be enough.)

B. Possible answer: Each can costs $4 ÷ 5 = $0.80 per can, so 48 cans of tomatoes would cost 48 × 0.80 = $38.40.

Answers to Problem 3.2 Follow-Up

1. Possible answer: The price per can at CannedStuff is $4 ÷ 5 = 80¢ per can. The price at EatMore is $6 ÷ 7 = about 86¢ per can. The tomatoes at CannedStuff are a better buy.

2. See page 36f.

Assignment Choices

ACE questions 3, 5, 6, 13–24, and unassigned choices from earlier problems

Sharing Pizza

At a Glance

Grouping:
pairs or small groups

Launch

- Make sure students understand what the problem is asking.

- Explain that you are most interested in their explanations about their work.

Explore

- In part A, encourage students to reason in more than one way.

- In part B, remind students about their earlier work with comparisons and ratios.

- Have groups work on the follow-up.

Summarize

- Have groups share how they thought about the problem.

- As a class, discuss the variety of solutions offered.

 Sharing Pizza

On the last day of camp, the cook served pizza. The camp dining room has two kinds of tables. A large table seats 10 people, and a small table seats 8 people. The cook tells the students who are serving dinner to put four pizzas on each large table and three pizzas on each small table.

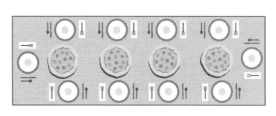
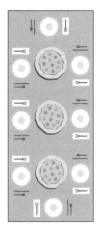

Problem 3.3

A. If the pizzas at a table are shared equally by everyone at the table, will a person sitting at a small table get the same amount of pizza as a person sitting at a large table? Explain your reasoning.

B. The ratio of large tables to small tables in the dining room is 8 to 5. There are exactly enough seats for the 240 campers. How many tables of each kind are there?

■ Problem 3.3 Follow-Up

1. How were ratios helpful in thinking about the problem?

2. How many pizzas will the cook need in order to put four on each large table and three on each small table?

Assignment Choices

ACE questions 4, 7, 8, 25, and unassigned choices from earlier problems

Answers to Problem 3.3

A. Campers sitting at a large table will receive more pizza than campers sitting at a small table. At a large table, ten campers get an equal share of 4 pizzas, or $\frac{4}{10} = \frac{2}{5}$ of a pizza. Similarly, a camper at a small table will get $\frac{3}{8}$ of a pizza.

B. There are 16 large tables and 10 small tables.

Answers to Problem 3.3 Follow-Up

1. Possible answer: In part A, ratios tell us the pizzas per person at each table. We compared the ratios to find which table allows more pizza per person. In part B, one ratio told us about the number of tables, 8 large tables to 5 small tables. Another ratio told us about people per table, 10 people per large table and 8 people per small table.

2. From the answer to 3.3B, we see that the cook will need $16 \times 4 = 64$ plus $10 \times 3 = 30$, or 94 pizzas.

As you work on these ACE questions, use your calculator whenever you need it.

Applications

1. At camp, Miriam learned how to use a pottery wheel. She can make 3 bowls in 2 hours. How long will it take her to make a set of 12 bowls?

2. The camp cook's favorite recipe for salad dressing calls for 2 tablespoons of lemon juice and 6 tablespoons of olive oil. If the cook wants to make a large batch of salad dressing using 3 cups of oil, how much lemon juice will he need? (There are 16 tablespoons in 1 cup.)

3. You need to buy several dozen avocados to make guacamole dip for a party. At the co-op, you can buy 7 avocados for $6.00. At the Cheapy Food Mart, 5 avocados cost $4.50. At which store will you get the better buy?

4. Friendly Food Store has Cocoa Blast cereal on sale this week at a price of $8.25 for five boxes. Best Food Store is offering the same size box of Cocoa Blast at a price of $3.50 for two boxes. Which offer gives you the most cereal for your money?

5. In the ads for Bolda Cola from Investigation 1, one possible concluding statement says "by a ratio of 3 to 2" and another says "by a ratio of 17,139 to 11,426." These ratios are equivalent. Write four other statements containing ratios equivalent to these ratios

---

Answers

Applications

1. See below left.

2. See below left.

3. At the co-op, avocados are $6.00 ÷ 7 = about 86¢ apiece. At the Cheapy Food Mart, they are $4.50 ÷ 5 = 90¢ apiece. The co-op has the better buy.

4. At Friendly Food, Cocoa Blast is $8.25 ÷ 5 = $1.65 per box. At Best Food, it is $3.50 ÷ 2 = $1.75 per box. Friendly Food Store offers more cereal for the money.

5. Possible answer: By a ratio of 6 to 4, 9 to 6, 12 to 8, and 15 to 10. (There is an infinite number of such pairs.)

---

1. If Miriam makes 3 bowls in 2 hours, she could make 6 bowls in 4 hours and 12 bowls in 8 hours. The following table represents the problem.

Bowls	3	6	9	12
Time (hours)	2	4	6	8

2. Since 3 cups of oil is 48 tablespoons of oil, the cook is making 48 ÷ 6 = 8 batches of dressing and needs 2 × 8 = 16 tablespoons, or 1 cup, of lemon juice. Or, since the ratio of lemon juice to oil is 1 to 3, and there are 3 cups of oil, 1 cup of lemon juice is needed. The following table represents the problem.

Lemon juice (tbs)	2	4	6	8	10	12	14	16
Oil (tbs)	6	12	18	24	30	36	42	48

6a. 18 to 12

6b. 12 to 18

6c. 18 to 30

6d. 30 to 18

7. At the small table, everyone will get 2 ÷ 5 = 0.40 or 40% of a pizza. At the medium table, everyone will get 3 ÷ 7 = 0.43 or 43% of a pizza. At the large table, everyone will get 5 ÷ 12 = 0.42 or 42% of a pizza. The numbers are so close that Lakisha should probably consider with whom she would like to sit.

8a. Elena uses nuggets to formula in a ratio of 4 cups to 6 cups, or 2 to 3, so she would need 2 × 6 = 12 cups of formula.

8b. Elena would need 3 × 3 = 9 cups of formula.

8c. Elena uses $\frac{3}{2}$ cups of formula per cup of nuggets, so she would need 7.5 ÷ 1.5 = 5 cups of nuggets.

6. At Louis Armstrong School, Ms. Turini's homeroom has 18 boys and 12 girls.

  a. What is the ratio of boys to girls in Ms. Turini's homeroom?

  b. What is the ratio of girls to boys?

  c. What is the ratio of boys to students in the class?

  d. What is the ratio of students in the class to boys?

7. Lakisha is attending a party at her favorite pizza parlor. Three tables are set up for the guests. After the pizzas are placed on the tables, the guests are asked to sit anywhere they choose. The small table has 5 seats and 2 pizzas, the medium table has 7 seats and 3 pizzas, and the large table has 12 seats and 5 pizzas. The pizzas at each table will be shared equally. Where should Lakisha sit if she is very hungry?

8. Elena works in the animal nursery at the county zoo. The baby monkeys eat a mixture of high-fiber nuggets and high-protein formula. Last month, Elena mixed 4 cups of nuggets and 6 cups of high-protein formula to make the food for each feeding. This month, the monkeys can eat more at each feeding.

  a. If Elena uses 8 cups of nuggets in the new mix, how much high-protein formula should she use?

  b. If Elena uses only 6 cups of nuggets, how much formula should she use?

  c. If Elena uses 7.5 cups of formula, how many cups of nuggets should she use?

In 9–11, use the apple juice recipes below.

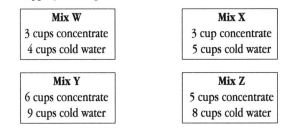

| Mix W |
| 3 cups concentrate |
| 4 cups cold water |

| Mix X |
| 3 cup concentrate |
| 5 cups cold water |

| Mix Y |
| 6 cups concentrate |
| 9 cups cold water |

| Mix Z |
| 5 cups concentrate |
| 8 cups cold water |

9. **a.** If you made a single batch of mix W, what fraction of the batch would be concentrate? Answer the same question for mixes X, Y, and Z.

b. Rewrite your answers to part a as percents.

10. Which recipe would make the most "appley" juice?

11. If you made only 1 cup of mix W, how much water and how much concentrate would you need? Answer the same question for mixes X, Y, and Z.

Connections

12. The diagram below illustrates the equivalence of two fractions. Find the missing numerator.

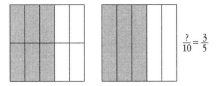

$$\frac{?}{10} = \frac{3}{5}$$

In 13–18, replace the question mark with a number to make a true statement.

13. $\frac{3}{15} = \frac{?}{30}$ **14.** $\frac{1}{2} = \frac{?}{20}$

15. $\frac{?}{20} = \frac{3}{5}$ **16.** $\frac{18}{30} = \frac{?}{15}$

17. $\frac{?}{15} = \frac{3}{5}$ **18.** $\frac{9}{15} = \frac{12}{?}$

9a. mix W: $\frac{3}{7}$; mix X: $\frac{3}{8}$; mix Y: $\frac{6}{15}$; mix Z: $\frac{5}{13}$

9b. mix W: 42.9%; mix X: 37.5%; mix Y: 40%; mix Z: 38.5%

10. Since mix W has the highest percentage of concentrate, it will taste most appley.

11. See below left.

Connections

12. $\frac{6}{10} = \frac{3}{5}$

13. $\frac{3}{15} = \frac{6}{30}$

14. $\frac{1}{2} = \frac{10}{20}$

15. $\frac{12}{20} = \frac{3}{5}$

16. $\frac{18}{30} = \frac{9}{15}$

17. $\frac{9}{15} = \frac{3}{5}$

18. $\frac{9}{15} = \frac{12}{20}$

11.

	Mix W	Mix X	Mix Y	Mix Z
Cups concentrate	$\frac{3}{7}$	$\frac{3}{8}$	$\frac{6}{15}$	$\frac{5}{13}$
Cups water	$\frac{4}{7}$	$\frac{5}{8}$	$\frac{9}{15}$	$\frac{8}{13}$

19. See below right.

20. $\frac{6}{14} = \frac{9}{21} = \frac{12}{28}$

21. $\frac{6}{27} = \frac{8}{36} = \frac{10}{45}$

22. $\frac{4}{20} = \frac{5}{25} = \frac{6}{30}$

23. $\frac{6}{8} = \frac{15}{20} = \frac{24}{32}$

Extensions

24a. Possible drawing of Twiggy:

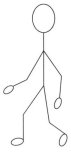

24b. Possible drawing of Branchy:

24c. See page 36g.

24d. Possible answer: The ratio of Mr. Stickman's height to Twiggy's height is 2 to 1. The ratio of Twiggy's height to Branchy's height is 3 to 2. The ratio of Mr. Stickman's height to Branchy's height is 3 to 1.

---

19. Illustrate your answer to question 13 by drawing a picture like the one in question 12.

In 20–23, replace the question marks with numbers to make a true statement.

20. $\frac{6}{14} = \frac{?}{21} = \frac{?}{28}$

21. $\frac{?}{27} = \frac{8}{36} = \frac{?}{45}$

22. $\frac{?}{20} = \frac{?}{25} = \frac{6}{30}$

23. $\frac{?}{8} = \frac{15}{?} = \frac{24}{32}$

Extensions

24. Here is a drawing of Mr. Stickman.

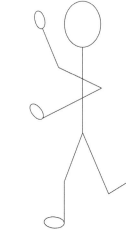

a. Draw a picture of Twiggy Stickman. She is $\frac{1}{2}$ as tall as Mr. Stickman.

b. Draw a picture of Branchy Stickman. He is $\frac{2}{3}$ as tall as Twiggy.

c. Branchy's height is what fraction of Mr. Stickman's height? Explain your reasoning.

d. Use some other form of comparison to rewrite the fraction comparisons in parts a, b, and c.

19.

$\frac{3}{15} = \frac{6}{30}$

25. a. What fraction of this square is shaded?

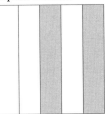

b. What fraction of this square is shaded?

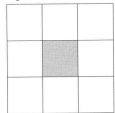

c. Draw a picture to show a fraction with a denominator of 10 that is equivalent to the fraction shaded in part a. Tell what fraction of your drawing is shaded.

d. Draw a picture to show a fraction with a denominator of 27 that is equivalent to the fraction shaded in part b. Tell what fraction of your drawing is shaded.

e. What percent of the square in part a is shaded?

f. What percent of the square in part b is shaded?

g. What is the ratio of the shaded area to the unshaded area in part a?

h. What is the ratio of the shaded area to the unshaded area in part b?

i. The squares in parts a and b are the same size. What is the ratio of the shaded part of the square in part a to the shaded part of the square in part b? Be careful–the answer is not 2 to 1.

25a. $\frac{2}{5}$

25b. $\frac{1}{9}$

25c. See below left.

25d. See below left.

25e. 40%

25f. 11.1%

25g. 2 to 3

25h. 1 to 8

25i. The ratio is $\frac{2}{5}$ to $\frac{1}{9}$.

25c. Possible drawing:

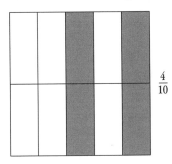

$\frac{4}{10}$

25d. Possible drawing:

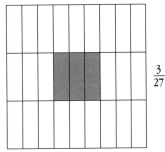

$\frac{3}{27}$

Possible Answers

1. If we know that there are 57 black beads and 33 red beads in a jar, we can say that the ratio of black beads to red beads in the jar is 57 to 33, which can also be written 57 black : 33 red. This is a part-to-part ratio comparison. We can also use ratios to compare the number of black beads to the total number of beads, which is 57 to 90, or 57 black : 90 total. This is a part-to-whole ratio comparison. Ratios can also be written in fraction form; we can say that $\frac{57}{90}$ of the beads are black. We can also write ratios as a percents; 63.3% of the beads are black.

2. See page 36g.

3. Since 60% of the juice is concentrate, 40% is water. This means that the concentrate-to-water ratio is 60 to 40, or 6 to 4, or 3 to 2.

4. Since the ratio of concentrate to water is 3 to 5, the fraction $\frac{3}{8}$ tells how much of the juice is concentrate. As a decimal, $\frac{3}{8}$ is 0.375, which means that 37.5% of the juice is concentrate.

Mathematical Reflections

In this investigation, you learned about ratios and about using ratios to make comparisons. These questions will help you summarize what you have learned:

1 Explain how to form a ratio and how ratios can be used to compare two numbers. Use examples to help explain your thinking.

2 What strategy can you use to compare two ratios? Be very specific. Your strategy should allow you to tell whether the two ratios are the same or different. Make up a problem that can be solved by using your strategy.

In Investigation 2, you used percents to make comparisons. In Investigation 3, you used ratios to make comparisons.

3 The percent of orange concentrate in a juice mix is 60%. What is the ratio of concentrate to water in the mix?

4 The ratio of concentrate to water in a juice mix is 3 to 5. What percent of the mix is concentrate?

Think about your answers to these questions, discuss your ideas with other students and your teacher, and then write a summary of your findings in your journal.

Tips for the Linguistically Diverse Classroom

Diagram Code The Diagram Code technique is described in detail in *Getting to Know Connected Mathematics*. Students use a minimal number of words and drawings, diagrams, or symbols to respond to questions that require writing. Example: Question 4—A student might answer this question by writing *3 to 8 = $\frac{3}{8}$;* below this, *$\frac{3}{8}$ = 0.375;* below this, *0.375 = 37.5%*.

TEACHING THE INVESTIGATION

3.1 • Mixing Juice

In the student edition, the investigation opens with six statements of comparison using ratios. The "Think about this!" focuses students' attention on the ratio comparisons, asking whether each ratio is a part-to-part ratio, a part-to-whole ratio, or a ratio comparing different kinds of measures or counts. The third statement compares a part to a whole. The fifth statement compares two different kinds of measures. The remaining statements compare parts to parts.

Students are then offered an example of how to scale a ratio up or down. Scaling ratios requires a kind of thinking similar to that students have used in their work with finding equivalent fractions. However, the ratios are written in the form 5:6 or 5 to 6 to help students separate the ideas of ratios from fraction arithmetic. It is just as valid to write ratios in fraction form, but we use the other notation in the beginning.

Before launching the problem, decide whether you want to pose the problem in a more open way and let students try to make sense of what they need to do to make the necessary comparisons or whether you want to give them a more in-depth introduction to ratios before they begin. An advantage to posing the problem in an open-ended way—allowing students to find their own ways to think about it—is that the discussion about ratios after students have developed some of their own ideas can be quite insightful and effective.

This is a challenging problem for students. Some teachers launch the problem, let groups begin work, and then reassemble the class to discuss the groups' initial ideas about the different mixes. This process gives groups a chance to consider several strategies. Some teachers discuss parts A and B as a class, then challenge groups to solve part C. The follow-up can be done as a class after the summary of the problem.

Launch

Introduce the orange juice problem by making sure students understand the context.

> How many of you have made orange juice from frozen concentrate?
> What did you have to do?

You may want to bring in a can of thawed orange juice concentrate and, with the class, make orange juice by following the instructions on the can. Talk about the ratio of concentrated juice to water, and point out that the four recipes in the problem differ from the one on the can (typically, 1 can of concentrate to 3 cans of water).

Explore

Have students work in groups of two to four. As they discuss parts A and B, circulate and ask questions. Ask groups to explain their conjectures about which recipe would make the most and the least orangey juice. If they are employing naive strategies—such as finding the difference between the number of cans of concentrate and ignoring the water altogether—challenge these ideas.

> Does that mean I can keep adding cans of water and *never* make the juice less orangey?

Other groups may propose the idea that, for example, $\frac{2}{3}$ of the juice made from mix A is concentrate. Help them reconsider this idea.

> How much orange juice does *one* recipe of mix A make?

Leave students to sort out what fraction of the juice in one recipe is actually concentrate. They will probably question their initial statement and recognize that the whole is 5 cups, so the fraction that is concentrate must be $\frac{2}{5}$, not $\frac{2}{3}$.

If groups are stumped by how to approach part C of the problem, the question of making enough orange juice for 240 people, ask them to consider mix A first.

> How much total liquid—concentrate and water—is in a single batch of mix A? *(5 cups)*

> Do you have any ideas about how many people this one batch of orange juice will serve? What if each serving were 8 ounces—the same as 1 cup? *(5 servings are possible.)* So, how many half-cup servings is this? *(10)*

> If you were going to serve orange juice to 50 people, how many batches of mix A would you need for each person to get a half cup of juice? What strategies might we use to answer this question?

Some students might divide 50 people by 10 servings per batch to determine that 5 batches are needed. Some may reason that if one batch makes 10 servings, then two batches make 20 servings, three batches make 30 servings, four batches make 40 servings, and five batches make 50 servings. This could be shown in a table.

Batches	1	2	3	4	5	6	7
Servings	10	20	30	40	50	60	70

You may also want to demonstrate how this information could be displayed in a drawing. A sketch of 10 glasses could represent each batch, showing that the number of servings must be a multiple of 10. Many of these ideas need to surface and be examined again in the summary.

Summarize

If you have chosen to present this problem in two stages, this will actually be your second summary of the problem. If so, revisit parts A and B as well as part C. You want students to leave this problem having encountered several problem-solving strategies, with an emphasis on ratios.

Call on students to share their ideas about parts A and B. They will likely have a variety of ways to reason about these questions. One way to express the relationship of *concentrate* to *total liquid* is to use part-to-whole ratios, express the ratios in fraction form, and then order the fractions (and thus the ratios) from smallest to largest. Students can then identify which mix is the most orangey (indicated by the most concentrate, or the largest fraction) and which is the least orangey.

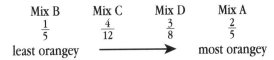

Mix B | Mix C | Mix D | Mix A
$\frac{1}{5}$ | $\frac{4}{12}$ | $\frac{3}{8}$ | $\frac{2}{5}$

least orangey ⟶ most orangey

Verify that students can explain the meaning of the corresponding fractions; for example, the $\frac{4}{12}$ for mix C means that 1 cup of orange juice contains $\frac{4}{12}$ of a cup of concentrate and $\frac{8}{12}$ of a cup of water. To compare these fractions, students may want to find a common denominator and rewrite the fractions (as $\frac{24}{120}$, $\frac{40}{120}$, $\frac{45}{120}$, and $\frac{48}{120}$). Or, using their prior knowledge of fractions, they may want to represent them as decimals (0.25, 0.33, 0.38, and 0.40).

For part C, again allow groups to share their results and strategies and explain why their results make sense. Here are four ways of reasoning that groups have suggested.

■ Geoffrey's group: "We found the number of recipes needed to make 120 cups of juice from each mix, then multiplied to find the total amounts of concentrate and water. For example, for mix A, one recipe makes 5 cups of juice. We divide 120 by 5 to get 24, the number of recipes needed. Since we need 2 cups of concentrate and 3 cups of water for one recipe, we need $2 \times 24 = 48$ cups of concentrate and $3 \times 24 = 72$ cups of water for 24 recipes."

■ Lamar's group: "We used a special strategy for mix C. Since 4 cups of concentrate to 8 cups of water is the same ratio as 1 cup of concentrate to 2 cups of water, we can picture the 120 cups of juice divided into three groups of 40 cups each. We need 1 part concentrate, which is 40 cups of concentrate. We need 2 parts water, which is 80 cups of water." (This strategy can be applied to the other mixes, but it usually evolves from reasoning about mix C.)

■ Pedro's group: "We made a table to help us scale up. This is our table for mix D:

Cups concentrate	3	6	9	12	15	18	21	24	27	30	33	36	39	42	45
Cups water	5	10	15	20	25	30	35	40	45	50	55	60	65	70	75

The sum of 45 and 75 is the 120 cups that we need, which means we need 45 cups of concentrate and 75 cups of water." (The strategy of making a table is clearly scaling ratios in the same way that students have found equivalent fractions.)

■ Chris's group: "We found a common denominator and then found equivalent fractions that represent the part of the whole that is concentrate."

Mix A | Mix B | Mix C | Mix D
$\frac{2}{5}$ | $\frac{1}{5}$ | $\frac{4}{12}$ | $\frac{3}{8}$
$\frac{48}{120}$ | $\frac{24}{120}$ | $\frac{40}{120}$ | $\frac{45}{120}$

(This is similar to the strategy required to solve parts A and B.)

To check students' thinking about this problem, ask:

Which of the following would taste most orangey: 2 cups of concentrate to 3 cups of water, 4 cups of concentrate to 6 cups of water, or 10 cups of concentrate to 15 cups of water? *(They would all taste the same.)*

If some groups are still struggling with these concepts, you may want to have them build visual representations of the ratio in one of the mixes. Distribute orange and white chips, cubes, or pieces of paper, and ask groups to use them to construct a physical model of the number of cups of concentrate and water needed to make enough juice for the 240 campers using mix B. Students should show 24 groups of chips, with 1 orange chip and 4 white chips in each group. When groups have finished, you might ask one or two to talk about how they built their representation. Make sure students see that as they add another recipe of juice to the model, they are keeping the ratio of concentrate to water constant.

Discuss each of the follow-up questions, giving students a chance to reflect on how they have used ratios in this problem.

3.2 • Helping the Cook

This problem again involves scaling up a recipe, a process that is mathematically equivalent to solving a proportion. Because we want students to develop a variety of flexible strategies for thinking about such problems, we offer them no explicit definition of a proportion nor any formal procedure for solving proportions.

Launch

To launch the problem, just make sure students have a clear understanding of the situation.

Explore

Let groups of two to four work on the problem and the follow-up, finding their own ways of reasoning about the solutions. As groups work, you have an opportunity to make an informal assessment of who understands and can apply ratio concepts and who is still struggling. Offer help where it is needed, reminding students to remember to properly label the numbers they are using (for example, 5 cans : $4.00) and to interpret the ratios, percents, and other forms of comparison in ways that fit the problem (5:4 means 5 cans for $4.00).

If some groups find answers to the two questions and follow-up very easily, encourage them to find other ways to think about the problem. (See the Summarize section for examples.)

Summarize

Let groups report their answers and talk about their strategies. One interesting aspect of this problem is how groups handled the range of people per can. Some groups may report a range figured from 5 people per can to 6 people per can; others may compute the answer for 5.5 people per can; and others may figure the answer for both 5 and 6 people per can, then average the results.

For part B, assuming 40 to 48 cans are needed, figuring the price of 40 cans is easy; they would cost the cook $4 \times 8 = $32. Computing the cost for 48 cans is a bit difficult, since 48 is not a multiple of 5. Look for a variety of ways of calculating the cost of those last 3 cans. Some students may say that they would buy 50 cans to avoid calculating the price for 3 cans.

Question 1 of the follow-up is a "better buy" problem. Again, the student-generated strategies will be interesting to discuss. Some groups may find the cost per can at each store and compare them; others may form ratios, find equivalent ratios, and compare them; others may just compute the cost for the cans at EatMore and compare it to their answer for part B of the problem. Whichever way they look at the problem, the CannedStuff offer is the better deal.

Watch for students who use inappropriate additive reasoning (such as reasoning that 5 for $4 is equivalent to 7 for $6 since, in each pair, the difference in the numbers is 1) rather than multiplicative reasoning (such as, at 5 for $4, you can buy 10 for $8, or 20 for $16).

In question 2, help students to understand that both *cans per dollar* and *dollars per can* are legitimate ratios—they just represent different things.

3.3 • Sharing Pizza

In this problem, students form ratios and then compare them to other ratios, an exercise that offers an intuitive introduction to proportion.

Launch

To engage students in the problem, you might describe the situation and display the diagram of the two kinds of tables on Transparency 3.3. Make sure students understand that the question is whether a student sitting at a large table and a student sitting at a small table will receive the same amount of pizza. Stress that what you are most interested in is each group's *explanation* of why they made the decisions they did.

Explore

By this time, most of your students should find the reasoning in part A easy. As students work in groups or pairs, encourage them to try to see more than one way to make the comparison. Say that you want to see how deeply they have thought about the problem reflected in their explanations. The numbers in the problem are relatively small, so the comparisons can be the focus of the activity.

Part B, which is basically a proportion problem, is more difficult; the strategies students developed in the orange juice problem will be helpful here. You may want to remind them to review their earlier work in Problem 3.1.

Once groups finish the problem, ask them to discuss the follow-up questions. If they are struggling with the problem, incorporate the follow-up questions into the end of the summary.

Summarize

Students will probably devise a variety of ways to reason about this problem. Let them present and question each other about their approaches. If some students reason that a person at a large table will get more, since a large table has more pizza; or that a person at a small table will get more, since there are fewer people to share pizza; help them to see that a single number—the number of people or the number of pizzas—does not supply enough information for making a reasonable decision. Present examples that address this idea.

> Suppose one table had 30 people and 5 pizzas and another had 5 people and 4 pizzas. If the pizza is shared equally at each table, where would you rather sit if you were very hungry? Why?
>
> If there were a table with 10 people and 5 pizzas and another with only 3 people and 1 pizza, where would you want to sit if you were very hungry? Why?

Two numbers are associated with each table—the number of pizzas *and* the number of people. Both values must be considered to make a reasonable comparison. It might be helpful for students to look at the rates of pizzas per person or of people per pizza. In the problem, the large table has 4 pizzas to be shared among 10 people; this is $\frac{4}{10}$ of a pizza per person. The small table has 3 pizzas to be shared among 8 people; this is $\frac{3}{8}$ of a pizza per person.

> If you want to dine at the table with the most pizza per person, where would you sit? In other words, how do $\frac{4}{10}$ (or $\frac{2}{5}$) and $\frac{3}{8}$ compare?

Students may have considered equivalent fractions, decimals, or percents. Using equivalent fractions, $\frac{2}{5} = \frac{16}{40}$ and $\frac{3}{8} = \frac{15}{40}$. Since $\frac{16}{40}$ is greater, a student would get more pizza at a large table. If students do not think of using percents, you may want to inquire about this.

> What percent of a pizza does a person at a large table get? *(40%)* What percent of a pizza does a person at a small table get? *(37.5%)*

Part B requires finding the number of tables, in a ratio equivalent to 8 large tables to 5 small tables, that would accommodate 240 campers. Ask groups to share their thinking about the question. If they were unable to find a solution, ask them to tell what they know for sure and why.

The complexity of this question is that we are working with two ratios. A large table seats 10 people, and a small table seats 8. One way to think about the question is to ask how many campers one "recipe" of tables—8 large and 5 small—would seat. The answer is 80 + 40 people, or 120 people, so we need two "recipes," or 16 large and 10 small tables.

Additional Answers

Answers to Problem 3.1

C. The table shows how much of each ingredient is needed to serve 240 people. (See possible explanations in the summary.)

	Mix A	Mix B	Mix C	Mix D
Ratio of concentrate to water	2 to 3	1 to 4	4 to 8	3 to 5
Number of batches	24	24	10	15
Cups concentrate	48	24	40	45
Cups water	72	96	80	75
Total cups of juice	120	120	120	120

Answers to Problem 3.1 Follow-Up

2.

	Mix A	Mix B	Mix C	Mix D
Cups concentrate	$\frac{2}{5}$	$\frac{1}{5}$	$\frac{4}{12}$	$\frac{3}{8}$
Cups water	$\frac{3}{5}$	$\frac{4}{5}$	$\frac{8}{12}$	$\frac{5}{8}$

Answers to Problem 3.2 Follow-Up

2. The 1.16666667 represents the number of cans per dollar. For each dollar spent, a customer receives $1\frac{1}{6}$ cans. The 0.85714286 represents the number of dollars per can. For each can purchased, a customer spends about 86¢. (Either form of reasoning is correct.)

ACE Answers

Extensions

24c. Branchy's height is $\frac{2}{3}$ of Twiggy's height, which is $\frac{1}{2}$ of Mr. Stickman's height, which makes Branchy $\frac{2}{6}$ or $\frac{1}{3}$ of Mr. Stickman's height.

For the Teacher: Reviewing ACE Question 24

You may want to review this problem and offer this sketch as a visual solution.

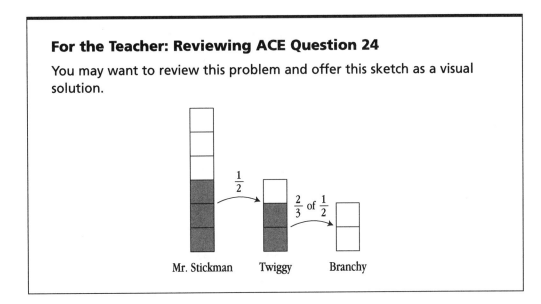

Mr. Stickman   Twiggy   Branchy

Mathematical Reflections

2. Two ratios can be compared by scaling them. For example, if we wanted to know which mix will have a stronger flavor—5 cans of grape concentrate and 3 cans of water or 7 cans of grape concentrate and 5 cans of water—we could compare the two ratios 5:3 and 7:5. If we scale the ratios, we get the following:

5:3	7:5
10:6	14:10
15:9	**21:15**
20:12	28:20
25:15	**35:25**
30:18	
35:21	

From this, we can compare ratios indicating the same amount of water, such as 25:15 and 21:15. This says that the first mix is more grapey, as it has more concentrate for the same amount of water. The table also shows two ratios with the same amount of concentrate, 35:21 and 35:25. This shows that we have the same amount of concentrate but more water in the second mix. The two ratios are obviously not the same.

You can also compare the ratios of a part to the whole:

5:3 becomes $\frac{5}{8}$ = 0.625 or 62.5% concentrate

7:5 becomes $\frac{7}{12}$ = 0.583 or 58.3% concentrate

Comparing by Finding Rates

In their work this year, students have already looked at tables, graphs, verbal descriptions, and symbols as ways to represent data. In this investigation, they connect proportional reasoning and unit rates to the notion of constant growth in tables and to straight lines in graphical representations, and they revisit earlier work with the relationship distance = rate $\times$ time. One of the important goals of this unit is not only to have students learn different ways to reason in proportional situations but to recognize *when* such reasoning is appropriate. Observing patterns in tables and graphs will help students develop ways to tell whether a situation involves proportion.

In Problem 4.1, Comparing Fuel Economy, students add the concepts of rates and unit rates to their strategies for reasoning about situations involving ratio and proportion. In Problem 4.2, Using Unit Rates, the idea of a unit rate is made explicit for the first time. Students compute unit rates for the vehicles in Problem 4.1 and encounter a strategy for reasoning with unit rates. Then they find rules, create rate tables and graphs, and look for patterns in the data. In Problem 4.3, Solving Problems with Rates, students compute how far a bicyclist has traveled and figure out what *constant* rate of speed would equal this performance. In Problem 4.4, Buying Beads, they encounter unit rates in a real-world setting as they write rules relating the cost of a purchase to the number of items bought.

Mathematical and Problem-Solving Goals

- **To find unit rates**

- **To represent data in tables and graphs**

- **To look for patterns in tables in order to make predictions beyond the tables**

- **To connect unit rates with the rule describing a situation**

- **To begin to recognize that constant growth in a table will give a straight-line graph**

- **To find the missing value in a proportion**

Materials		
Problem	**For students**	**For the teacher**
All	Graphing calculators	Transparencies 4.1 to 4.4 (optional)
4.3	Centimeter grid paper, transparencies of centimeter grid paper and transparency markers (optional)	
ACE	Centimeter grid paper	

Student Pages 37–51   **Teaching the Investigation 51a–51h**

Comparing by Finding Rates

In this unit, you have been using percents and ratios to make comparisons. Now, look at these examples of a special kind of comparison you probably encounter frequently:

My mom's new car gets 45 miles per gallon on the expressway.

We need two sandwiches for each person at the picnic.

I earn $3.50 per hour baby-sitting for my neighbor.

Tomatoes are on sale five for $4.00.

The sign above the mystery meat in the cafeteria says 355 calories : 6 ounces.

James can run at a rate of 8.5 kilometers per hour.

Each statement above compares two *different* things: miles to gallons, sandwiches to people, dollars to hours, tomatoes to dollars, calories to ounces, and kilometers to hours. Comparisons of two different things, like those in the statements above, are called **rates.** They tell us the *rate* at which something happens.

4.1

Comparing Fuel Economy

Launch

- Introduce the idea of comparing by using rates, and talk about cars, gas mileage, and the story of Madeline and Luis.

Explore

- If pairs are having trouble, have them review the introduction to rates in the student edition.

- Remind students that your interest is in their explanations of their solution.

- Encourage students to explore a variety of strategies.

Summarize

- Have pairs share their solutions and explanations, and ask for alternative methods of solving the problem.

- Discuss the use of percents in this problem.

Assignment Choices

ACE questions 4, 5, and unassigned choices from earlier problems

---

You can scale a rate up or down to find an equivalent rate. For example, consider this problem:

> Ms. Balog's car gets 45 miles to the gallon on the highway. How much gas will the car use if Ms. Balog drives it 180 miles on the interstate?

Here are two ways you might solve this problem:

Method 1
Divide 180 by 45 to find out how many groups of 45 there are in 180. The result is 4, which means the car will use 4 gallons of gas.

Method 2
Write a ratio and scale up to find the answer:

45 miles per gallon means	45 miles : 1 gallon
or	90 miles : 2 gallons
or	135 miles : 3 gallons
or	180 miles : 4 gallons

The car will use 4 gallons of gas.

4.1 Comparing Fuel Economy

After graduating from the University of Colorado, Luis and Madeline both got teaching jobs in Denver. They each bought a new car for commuting to work, and one afternoon they had a friendly argument about whose car was better. Luis claimed his car was more fuel-efficient. Madeline challenged him to prove his claim. Since they would both be traveling home for Thanksgiving, Luis suggested they use their trips to test the gas mileage of their cars.

Madeline and Luis are from different small towns in southern Colorado, but the routes from Denver to both towns follow I-25 for the first 190 miles to Trinidad.

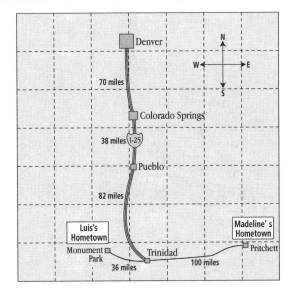

When the two friends returned from the holiday, they compared their fuel economy. Madeline's car used 19 gallons for the trip from Denver to Pritchett and back. Luis's car used only 15.5 gallons of gas for the trip from Denver to Monument Park and back. He said this proved his car was more fuel-efficient than Madeline's. Madeline disagreed.

Problem 4.1

Use the gasoline and mileage data to help settle Madeline and Luis's argument.

Which car do you think is more fuel-efficient on the highway? Explain how you decided and why you think you are correct.

▒ Problem 4.1 Follow-Up

Would it make sense to use percents to settle this argument? If so, show how; if not, explain why.

Answer to Problem 4.1

Madeline drove 2 × 290 = 580 miles, so her gas mileage was 580 miles ÷ 19 gallons = 30.5 mpg. Luis drove 2 × 226 = 452 miles, so his gas mileage was 452 miles ÷ 15.5 gallons = 29.2 mpg. Madeline's car is more fuel-efficient on the highway.

Answer to Problem 4.1 Follow-Up

We could write the gas mileage figures as percents, but they wouldn't help Madeline and Luis settle their argument because they would be quite difficult to interpret.

At a Glance

Grouping:
small groups

Launch

- Talk with students about the CD sale examples.

- Read the problem and follow-up with the class.

Explore

- As groups work, ask questions to help them better understand unit rates.

- If students are stuck on the follow-up, refer them to the *Variables and Patterns* student edition.

Summarize

- Discuss the groups' findings.

- Talk with students about the patterns in the rate table.

- Compare the graphs drawn for the follow-up.

- Help students connect the ideas of unit rates, rate tables, equations, and graphs.

Assignment Choices

ACE questions 1, 6, 10, 11, 17–20, and unassigned choices from earlier problems

The advertisements below use rates to describe sale prices. How would you compare the value of the offers described in the two ads?

One way to compare rates like these is to do some division to find unit rates. **Unit rates** are rates in which one of the numbers is 1 unit. For example, 55 miles per hour is a unit rate because it tells the number of miles driven for every 1 hour, and 99¢ a pound is a unit rate because it tells the cost for every 1 pound.

Think about this!

ook back at the examples at the beginning of this investigation. Which of these statements are examples of unit rates?

You can compare the advertisements above by finding the *price per CD* (that is, the price for 1 CD) at each store. The price per CD is $5.99 at Music City and $5.71 at CD World.

Problem 4.2

When Madeline and Luis compared the fuel economy of their new cars, they found these rates:

Madeline's car went 580 miles with 19 gallons of gasoline.
Luis's car went 452 miles with 15.5 gallons of gasoline.

Use this information to answer the following questions.

A. For each car, find a unit rate describing the mileage. Which car got better gas mileage? In other words, which car went more miles per gallon of gas?

B. Complete a table like the one below, showing the fuel used and the miles covered by each car based on the unit rates you found in part A. We call this kind of table a *rate table*.

Gallons of gas	0	1	2	3	4	5	6	7	8
Miles in Madeline's car									
Miles in Luis's car									

C. Look at the patterns in your table. For each car, write an equation for a rule you can use to predict the miles driven (*m*) from the gallons of gas used (*g*).

D. Use the rules you wrote in part C to find the number of miles each car could cover if it used 9.5, 15.5, 19, 23.8, 100, 125, and 150 gallons of gasoline.

▦ Problem 4.2 Follow-Up

1. Use your data from B or D to sketch graphs of the (gallons, miles) data for each car.
2. How are your two graphs alike? How are they different?
3. What do you think makes the two graphs different?

Answers to Problem 4.2

A. Madeline's car went 30.5 miles per gallon of gas, and Luis's car only went 29.2 miles per gallon. Madeline's car went 1.3 miles further on 1 gallon of gas and thus has the better gas mileage.

B. See page 51f.

C. Madeline's car: $m = 30.5g$; Luis's car: $m = 29.2g$

D. See page 51f.

Answers to Problem 4.2 Follow-Up

See page 51f.

Solving Problems with Rates

**Grouping:
small groups**

Launch

- Read or tell the story of Sascha's bicycle ride.

- Make sure students understand what the questions are asking.

Explore

- If groups are having trouble, ask questions to help them clarify what they know and what they need to find out.

- Distribute transparent grids to groups with particularly good graphs. *(optional)*

Summarize

- Have groups share their answers and strategies.

- Help the class analyze the graphs.

- Discuss the follow-up question.

4.3 **Solving Problems with Rates**

Suppose Sascha, a champion bicyclist, wants to see how far he can travel in an hour. He starts timing himself when he reaches a speed of 45 miles per hour. He maintains this speed for 10 minutes. Sascha starts to feel tired and slows down to 30 miles per hour for the next 5 minutes. He then reduces his speed to 25 miles per hour for the next 30 minutes. Finally, Sascha feels exhausted as he finishes the last 15 minutes at 15 miles per hour.

> **Problem 4.3**
>
> **A.** Make a graph showing Sascha's total distance traveled over time. Use 5-minute time intervals on the *x*-axis.
>
> **B.** How far did Sascha travel in his 1-hour ride? Explain.
>
> **C.** If you could maintain a steady speed of 13 miles per hour on a bike, how long would it take you to travel the same distance Sascha traveled in his 1-hour ride?
>
> **D.** If you were racing Sascha, what constant (steady) speed would you have to maintain to tie him?

■ **Problem 4.3 Follow-Up**

Can you write a single equation that will allow you to predict Sascha's total distance at any time during his 1-hour ride? Why or why not?

> ### Did you know?
>
> The highest speed ever recorded on a pedal-powered bike was 152.284 miles per hour. John Howard performed this amazing feat on July 20, 1985, at Bonneville Salt Flats, Utah. He was able to reach this speed by following a car, which acted as a windshield for him and his bike.
>
> Source: *Guinness Book of Records 1994.* Ed. Peter Matthews. New York: Bantam Books, 1994, p. 615.

Assignment Choices

ACE questions 2, 3, 8, 9, 21, and unassigned choices from earlier problems

Answers to Problem 4.3

A. See page 51g.

B. From the graph, we can see that Sascha traveled 26.25 mi.

C. See page 51g.

D. To tie Sascha, you would need to travel 26.25 mi in 1 h, or 26.25 mph.

Answer to Problem 4.3 Follow-Up

You cannot write one equation that will predict Sascha's total distance at any time during his ride, because his speed changes. Any rule that would work at one speed would not work at another.

4.4 Buying Beads

Stores often use rates in their advertisements. Rather than using unit rates, advertisements often give the cost for several items. For example, a grocery store might advertise five cans of tomatoes for $4.00. Such advertisements may entice customers to buy more. But, even though an ad gives the price for several items, you can usually buy fewer items at the same rate.

The owner of a crafts store believes that price displays like the one below get her customers' attention. However, when customers want amounts other than 10, 15, or 20 beads, figuring the bill is not easy.

Craft Beads
Spheres: 12¢ for 20
Cubes: 12¢ for 15
Cylinders: 8¢ for 10

Problem 4.4

Write an equation relating the cost (c) and the number of beads (x) for each type of bead:

Spheres: $c =$ _____

Cubes: $c =$ _____

Cylinders: $c =$ _____

■ Problem 4.4 Follow-Up

For each type of bead, you could find two unit rates. You could find the number of beads for each unit of cost (in other words, for each cent), and you could find the cost for each bead.

1. Which unit rate would be most useful if you were trying to figure out the number of beads you could buy with a certain amount of money?
2. Which unit rate would be most useful if you were trying to figure out how much money a certain number of beads costs?

Buying Beads

▪▪▪▪▪▪▪▪
At a Glance

Grouping: pairs

Launch

■ Talk with the class about the craft store owner's price display.

Explore

■ As pairs of students work, ask questions to help them refine their ideas.

Summarize

■ Have students share their strategies for solving the problem.

■ Offer another problem as a quick check on understanding.

■ Talk about the follow-up questions.

Assignment Choices

ACE questions 7, 12–16, 22, 23, and unassigned choices from earlier problems

Assessment

It is appropriate to use Check-Up 2 and the quiz after this problem.

Answer to Problem 4.4

Using the rate $\frac{\text{cost for given number of beads}}{\text{number of beads}}$, with c in cents, the equations are as follows:

Spheres: $c = \frac{12}{20}x$ or $c = \frac{3}{5}x$
Cubes: $c = \frac{12}{15}x$ or $c = \frac{4}{5}x$
Cylinders: $c = \frac{8}{10}x$ or $c = \frac{4}{5}x$

Answers to Problem 4.4 Follow-Up

1. To figure out how many beads you could buy with a certain amount of money, it would be more useful to know the number of beads you would get for each penny.

2. To figure out how much money a certain number of beads would cost, it would be more useful to know the cost per bead.

Answers

Applications

1a. See below right.

1b. See answer to question 2b on page 51g.

1c. The unit rate is 10 pounds of milk to 1 pound of cheddar cheese: $m = 10c$.

1d. Possible answer: The graph shows visually how the amounts of milk and cheese are related. From the rate table, you can easily look up an amount of milk and see the related amount of cheese. You can use the rule to calculate the amount of milk needed to produce any amount of cheese.

2a. See below right.

2b. See page 51g.

2c. The unit rate is 7 pounds of milk to 1 pound of cottage cheese: $m = 7c$.

2d. Possible answer: Both graphs are straight lines and cross at the point (0, 0). The cottage cheese graph is steeper than the cheddar cheese graph, because cheddar cheese requires more milk per pound than does cottage cheese. They are both straight lines.

As you work on these ACE questions, use your calculator whenever you need it.

Applications

1. The manager of Quality Dairy stores says it takes 1000 pounds of milk to make 100 pounds of cheddar cheese.

   a. Make a rate table showing the amount of milk needed to make 100 pounds to 1000 pounds of cheddar cheese in increments of 100 pounds (this means 100 pounds, 200 pounds, 300 pounds, and so on).

   b. Make a graph showing the relationship between pounds of milk and pounds of cheddar cheese. Think carefully about which variable should go on each axis.

   c. Find a unit rate relating pounds of milk to pounds of cheddar cheese. Use the rate you find to write an equation relating pounds of milk (m) to pounds of cheese (c).

   d. Give one advantage of each form of representation—the graph, the table, and the rule.

2. The Quality Dairy manager said it takes 700 pounds of milk to make 100 pounds of cottage cheese.

   a. Make a rate table showing the amount of milk needed to make 100 pounds to 1000 pounds of cottage cheese in increments of 100 pounds.

   b. Make a graph showing the relationship between pounds of milk and pounds of cottage cheese. Think carefully about which variable should go on each axis.

   c. Find a unit rate relating pounds of milk to pounds of cottage cheese. Use the rate you find to write an equation relating pounds of milk (m) to pounds of cottage cheese (c).

   d. Compare the graph in this question to the graph in question 1. Explain how they are alike and how they are different. What is the cause of the differences between the two graphs?

1a.

Milk (pounds)	1000	2000	3000	4000	5000	6000	7000	8000	9000	10,000
Cheddar cheese (pounds)	100	200	300	400	500	600	700	800	900	1000

2a.

Milk (pounds)	700	1400	2100	2800	3500	4200	4900	5600	6300	7000
Cottage cheese (pounds)	100	200	300	400	500	600	700	800	900	1000

3. The world-champion milk producer in 1993 was a 6-year-old cow from Oxford, New Hampshire. The cow, Tullando Royalty Maxima, produced 58,952 pounds of milk in that year!

a. Look back at your answers to question 2. How much cottage cheese could be made from the milk that Maxima produced during 1993?

b. The average weight of a dairy cow is 1400 pounds. How many dairy cows would be needed to equal the weight of the cottage cheese made from Maxima's yearly production of milk?

c. One gallon of milk weighs about 8.6 pounds. Suppose a milk bucket holds about 3 gallons. About how many milk buckets would Maxima's *daily* production of milk fill?

d. One pound of milk fills about two glasses. About how many glasses of milk could you fill with Maxima's *daily* production of milk?

3a. Since 7 pounds of milk will make 1 pound of cottage cheese, 58,952 ÷ 7 = about 8422 pounds of cottage cheese could be produced from Maxima's milk in 1993.

3b. Since 8422 ÷ 1400 = 6.02, it would take about 6 cows to balance this quantity of cottage cheese.

3c. One milk bucket will hold 3 × 8.6 = 25.8 pounds of milk. Maxima produces about 58,952 ÷ 365 = 161.5 pounds of milk per day, or about 161.5 ÷ 25.8 = 6.3 buckets of milk per day.

3d. Maxima produces about 161.5 × 2 = 323 glasses of milk per day.

4. Golda's speed is 10 mi ÷ 15 min = 0.67 mi/min. Dale's speed is 23 mi ÷ 30 min = 0.77 mi/min. Dale is faster.

5. Rolanda rode at a rate of 8 mi ÷ 32 min = 0.25 mi/min. Louise rode at 2 mi ÷ 10 min = 0.2 mi/min. Rolanda rode faster.

6. Fasiz is traveling at a rate of $\frac{8}{24} = \frac{1}{3}$ km/min. At this rate, Kari would drive 2 km in 6 min.

7a. The buses traveled 6 mi in 10 min, so going 18 mi would take $3 \times 10 = 30$ min.

7b. In 15 min, the buses would go $1.5 \times 6 = 9$ mi.

8. See below right.

4. On their morning commutes to work, Golda travels 10 miles in about 15 minutes and Dale travels 23 miles in about 30 minutes. Who has the faster average speed?

5. Rolanda and Louise rode bikes at a steady pace along a narrow road with no traffic. Rolanda rode 8 miles in 32 minutes. Louise rode 2 miles in 10 minutes. Who was riding the fastest?

6. Fasiz and Kari were driving at the same speed along a bumpy country road. Fasiz drove 8 kilometers in 24 minutes. How far did Kari drive in 6 minutes?

7. Students at Langston Hughes School rode to camp on several buses. On the long dirt road leading to the camp, the buses covered only 6 miles in 10 minutes.

    a. At this speed, how long would it take the buses to cover 18 miles?

    b. At this speed, how far would the buses go in 15 minutes?

8.   **a.** Mara's car can be driven 580 miles with 20 gallons of gasoline. Make a rate table showing the number of miles her car can be driven with 1, 2, 3, . . . , 10 gallons of gas.

    b. Joel's car can be driven 450 miles with 15 gallons of gasoline. Make a rate table showing the number of miles his car can be driven with 1, 2, 3, . . . , 10 gallons of gas.

8a.   580 mi on 20 gallons of gas is a unit rate of 29 mpg.

Gallons of gas	1	2	3	4	5	6	7	8	9	10
Miles driven	29	58	87	116	145	174	203	232	261	290

8b.   450 mi on 15 gallons of gas is a unit rate of 30 mpg.

Gallons of gas	1	2	3	4	5	6	7	8	9	10
Miles driven	30	60	90	120	150	180	210	240	270	300

9. The local grocery store has videotapes on sale, $3.00 for 2 tapes. You have $20.

   a. How many tapes can you buy?

   b. If there is a 7% sales tax on the tapes, how many can you buy?

Connections

10. Franky's Fudge Factory provides customers with the following information about the calories in their fudge.

Caloric Content of Franky's Fudge

Grams of fudge	Calories
50	150
150	450
300	900
500	1500

   a. Fiona ate 75 grams of fudge. How many calories did she consume?

   b. Freddy consumed 1000 calories worth of fudge. How many grams of fudge did he eat?

   c. Describe a rule you can use to find the number of calories in any number of grams of Franky's fudge.

11. This table shows how to convert liters to quarts.

Liters	Quarts
1	1.06
4	4.24
5	5.30
9	9.54

   a. About how many liters are in 5.5 quarts?

   b. About how many quarts are in 5.5 liters?

   c. Write an equation that relates liters (L) and quarts (Q).

10c. The rate describing the situation is 3 calories per 1 gram of fudge, so (number of calories) = 3 × (number of grams). Some students may construct a graph to find the rule:

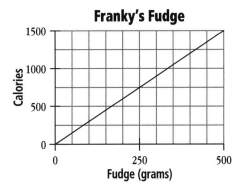

Franky's Fudge

9a. Each tape costs $3.00 ÷ 2 = $1.50. With $20, you can buy 20.00 ÷ 1.50 = 13.33 tapes, or 13 tapes with $0.50 remaining.

9b. Possible answers: On 13 tapes, the sales tax would be $19.50 × 0.07 = $1.36 or $1.37. You would not have enough to pay the sales tax. If you bought 12 tapes, the sales tax would be $18.00 × 0.07 = $1.26. The total cost would be $18.00 + 1.26 = $19.26. Or, since each tape has a sales tax of $1.50 × 0.07 = 10.5¢, each tape costs $1.605, so you can buy $20.00 ÷ $1.605 = 12 tapes.

Connections

10a. Since 150 g of fudge contains 450 cal, 75 g would contain 225 cal. (Note: You may want to bring in some fudge so students can get a sense of what 50 g looks like.)

10b. 1000 cal is $\frac{2}{3}$ of 1500 cal, so Freddy ate $\frac{2}{3}$ × 500 g = about 333 g of fudge.

10c. See below left.

11a. There are 1 ÷ 1.06 = 0.94 L per quart, so 5.5 qt is 5.5 × 0.94 = about 5.19 L.

11b. In 5.5 L there are 5.5 × 1.06 = 5.83 qt.

11c. From the unit rates, $Q = 1.06L$ and $L = 0.94Q$.

12. unit rate: 0.6 of a cent per bead; equation: price = 0.6 × number of beads

13. unit rate: 0.8 of a cent per nail; equation: price = 0.8 × number of nails

14. unit rate: 30 miles per gallon; equation: number of miles = 30 × number of gallons

15. unit rate: 1.5 cups of water per cup of concentrate; equation: amount of water = 1.5 × amount of concentrate

16. unit rate: $0.80 per can of soup; equation: price = 0.80 × number of cans of soup

17. $\frac{4}{9} \times 3 = 1\frac{1}{3}$

18. 40 × 2.25 = 90

19. Possible answer: $\frac{13}{4} \times \frac{16}{5} = 10\frac{2}{5}$

20. Possible answer: 0.38 × 4.36 = 1.6568

21a. Percents were calculated for boys, girls, and all students in each category. Then the percents were stacked on top of each other in the same order to show the whole 100%.

21b. The table gives the exact measures, so you can easily make comparisons. The bar graph is a quick, visual way of comparing the amount of time spent in each category by each group. Comparing the heights of corresponding bands is a quick way to compare the different groups.

In 12–16, find a unit rate, and use it to write an equation relating the two variables.

12. 12 cents for 20 beads

13. 8 cents for 10 nails

14. 450 miles on 15 gallons of gasoline

15. 3 cups of water for 2 cups of orange concentrate

16. $4.00 for 5 cans of soup

In 17 and 18, replace the question mark with a number to make a true sentence.

17. $\frac{4}{9} \times ? = 1\frac{1}{3}$

18. $? \times 2.25 = 90$

19. Write two fractions whose product is between 10 and 11.

20. Write two decimals whose product is between 1 and 2.

21. The table of data below shows the mean times that students in one seventh grade class spend on several activities during the weekend.

a. The *stacked bar graph* on the next page was made using the data from the table. Explain how it was constructed.

b. Suppose you are writing a report summarizing the class's data. You have space for either the table or the graph, but not both. What is one advantage of including the table? What is one advantage of including the stacked bar graph?

How We Spend Our Weekends

Category	Boys	Girls	All students
Sleeping	18.8 hours	18.2 hours	18.4 hours
Eating	4.0 hours	2.7 hours	3.5 hours
Recreation	7.8 hours	6.9 hours	7.4 hours
Talking on the phone	0.5 hours	0.7 hours	0.6 hours
Watching TV	4.2 hours	3.0 hours	3.7 hours
Doing chores, homework	3.6 hours	5.8 hours	4.7 hours
Other	9.1 hours	10.7 hours	9.7 hours

Extensions

22a. See below left.

22b. $n = 240 \div v$

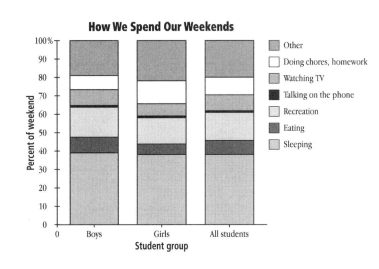

How We Spend Our Weekends

Legend:
- Other
- Doing chores, homework
- Watching TV
- Talking on the phone
- Recreation
- Eating
- Sleeping

Y-axis: Percent of weekend

X-axis: Student group (Boys, Girls, All students)

Extensions

22. A cider mill has pressed a 240-liter vat of apple juice. The mill has many kinds of containers in which to pack juice.

a. The mill owner wants to package the entire vat of juice in containers of the same size. Complete this table to show the number of containers of each size needed to hold the entire vat of juice.

Volume of container (liters)	10	4	2	1	$\frac{1}{2}$	$\frac{1}{4}$	$\frac{1}{10}$
Number of containers needed	24						

b. Write an equation that describes the relationship between the volume of the container (v) and the number of containers needed (n) to hold 240 liters of juice.

22a.

Volume of container (liters)	10	4	2	1	$\frac{1}{2}$	$\frac{1}{4}$	$\frac{1}{10}$
Number of containers needed	24	60	120	240	480	960	2400

23a. In 400 g of rust, she would find $70 \times 4 = 280$ g of iron and $30 \times 4 = 120$ g of oxygen.

23b. This ratio is constant: 0.7 g of iron per 1 g of rust.

23. A chemistry student is analyzing the contents of rust, and she finds that it is made of iron and oxygen. She tests several amounts of rust and produces the following data. (Note: g is the abbreviation for grams.)

Amount of rust (g)	Amount of iron (g)	Amount of oxygen (g)
50	35.0	15.0
100	70.0	30.0
135	94.5	40.5
150	105.0	45.0

a. If the student analyzed 400 grams of rust, how much iron and how much oxygen would she find?

b. Is the ratio of the amount of iron to the amount of rust constant? If so, what is the ratio?

Mathematical Reflections

In this investigation, you learned about a special way to compare quantities called a *rate*. You learned to compare rates, to find unit rates, and to use rates to make tables and graphs and to write equations. These questions will help you summarize what you have learned:

1 Give three examples of rates.

2 How can rates or unit rates help you to make comparisons?

3 How do you convert a rate to a unit rate? Illustrate your answer with one of the examples you gave in part 1.

4 How can information about unit rates be used to make tables and graphs showing how two variables are related? Use your example to illustrate your answer.

5 How can a unit rate be used to write an equation relating two variables? Use your example to illustrate your answer.

Think about your answers to these questions, discuss your ideas with other students and your teacher, and then write a summary of your findings in your journal.

Tips for the Linguistically Diverse Classroom

Diagram Code The Diagram Code technique is described in detail in *Getting to Know Connected Mathematics*. Students use a minimal number of words and drawings, diagrams, or symbols to respond to questions that require writing. Example: Question 1—A student might answer this question by drawing a page of math computation problems (labeled *3 problems per hour*), a stick figure mowing the lawn (labeled *$5 per hour*), and a black storm cloud (*labeled 1 inch rain in the fall*).

TEACHING THE INVESTIGATION

• **Comparing Fuel Economy**

Although we are quite accustomed as adults to dealing with mileage data in unit rate form (miles per gallon), there are several strategies that are feasible for solving problems involving mileage. Encourage students to explore a variety of methods. Students will likely apply the ideas of rates and unit rates. These concepts have not yet been formally presented, but are natural ways of thinking.

Launch

To introduce the topic of rates, refer to the statements on the introductory page of Investigation 4 in the student edition. Ask students to interpret each of the statements.

> In each statement, what is being compared? Are the two quantities the same kinds of measures or counts, or are they different?

Talk to students about their experiences with cars and travel.

> Do you know any drivers who worry about gas mileage? What does *gas mileage* mean? Do you know the gas mileage of any of your family's or friends' vehicles?

Try to elicit from the class the idea that fuel-efficient cars are cars that get relatively more miles per unit of gas.

Tell the story of Madeline and Luis, who are driving separate cars to visit their hometowns during Thanksgiving. You might want to display Transparency 4.1 and review the route that each driver will take. Then, pose the question:

> Whose car is more fuel-efficient on the highway?

Explore

Have students work in pairs on the problem and follow-up. If some pairs are struggling, ask them to review the discussion about rates and the example about Ms. Balog's car on page 38 of the student edition.

Remind students that you are interested in their *explanations* of how they arrived at their decisions. Why do they think their answers are correct?

Summarize

Have pairs report their answers and share how they thought about the problem. As always, ask them to present any alternative ways of thinking about the problem.

In any solution, students should take into account two quantities: gallons used and miles traveled. The ratio of total miles to total gallons is typically used to report fuel efficiency and commonly represented as miles per gallon (mpg).

Some students may compute gallons per mile and make perfectly good sense out of these rates. Miles per gallon is more common, but gallons per mile (gpm) is fine as long as students can explain what rate they have computed and what it means. Madeline's car uses $19 \div 580 =$ 0.033 gallons of gas per mile, and Luis's car uses $15.5 \div 452 = 0.034$ gallons of gas per mile, so Madeline's car uses less gas per mile.

Discuss the follow-up question. Remember that one major goal of the *Comparing and Scaling* unit is for students to begin to be selective about what kinds of situations can be best compared or described using a particular strategy. Since this problem is comparing two very different kinds of things—miles traveled and gallons of gas consumed—it is not easy to interpret what a percent would mean. Percents are most useful when we are comparing a part to a whole. This does not mean that we could not take the numbers in the problem, divide them to get a decimal, and write the decimal as a percent. We can always do this with two numbers. The trick, however, is understanding what the decimal or percent means in the context of the problem.

4.2 • Using Unit Rates

The idea of finding a value or cost for *one* item, and then using that information to develop further information or to solve problems, is useful in many contexts. In this problem, students explore the unit rate miles per gallon.

Launch

To introduce the topic of unit rates, you might refer again to the statements on the introductory page of Investigation 4.

> Which of the rates tell us how many of one thing are matched to just one of the second thing? *(miles per gallon, sandwiches per person, dollars per hour, and kilometers per hour)*

> These are a special type of rate called a unit rate. A *unit rate* tells us how many per unit. Miles per hour tells how many miles are matched with 1 hour of travel.

The two ads for CD sales will help focus students on the concept of unit rates. For many students, the natural way to compare the two offers is to find the two unit prices (or unit rates) and compare them. You might introduce the topic of this investigation by posing the CD comparison problem. Allow students time to think about it, then ask them to share their ideas.

Read Problem 4.2 with the class, and discuss the challenge of finding the more fuel-efficient car by comparing unit rates. If students already found and used this strategy in Problem 4.1, continue the discussion, asking them to make a table and to write rules to represent the problem. Talk with students about their experiences with creating tables to present information about two related things. (This can be a good review of ideas from the *Variables and Patterns* unit.)

> Where have you seen tables like this being used?

In the follow-up, students will create graphs of the data and discuss how their graphs compare.

Explore

Put students in groups of three or four to work on the problem and follow-up. As you circulate among the groups, ask questions to help students focus on the meaning of a unit rate and how it can be used to generate rate tables, rules, and graphs.

> If we know that Madeline's car traveled 580 miles on 19 gallons of gas, how can we find out how far her car will travel on 1 gallon of gas?
>
> How can you use your answer to help fill in the rate table?
>
> Do you see any patterns in your rate table? How would you describe them?
>
> Does the unit rate help you to write a rule that will predict the number of miles for *any* number of gallons of gas? If so, how?

If students have difficulty writing the rules in part C, have them state in words how they can use the unit rate to find the miles traveled for a given amount of gas. Their verbal descriptions should lead them to the rules. If they can't remember how to construct graphs and compare results, suggest that they search for examples in the *Variables and Patterns* student edition.

Summarize

Have groups share their findings. Examine the rate table as a class, and ask students what patterns they see in the data. (This is a chance to review the representations that were studied in the *Variables and Patterns* unit.) Here are some patterns students have noticed:

■ Doubling the number of miles doubles the amount of gas needed.

■ Tripling the number of gallons of gas triples the number of miles traveled.

Rates are often expressed as unit rates—the total number of miles traveled per unit (1 gallon) of gasoline. Madeline drove 580 miles and used 19 gallons of gas, which is a gas mileage of 30.5 mpg. Luis drove 452 miles and used 15.5 gallons of gas, a gas mileage of 29.2 mpg. In unit rates, Madeline travels about 30.5 miles on 1 gallon of gas, and Luis travels about 29.2 miles on 1 gallon of gas. Using unit rates is such a powerful way of comparing situations that involve ratios that students should begin to notice when it is appropriate.

Discuss the follow-up. (This is the first time in this unit that students are asked to compare two straight-line graphs. They did this for the first time in *Variables and Patterns*.) Students may or may not have language to describe the difference in the way the lines rise from left to right on the graph. (This is fine; they will study this idea in depth in the *Moving Straight Ahead* unit.) You might ask which line is steeper. This concept is in their experience and is a reasonable way to talk about how the lines differ.

4.3 • Solving Problems with Rates

This investigation plants seeds that will have a valuable harvest: relationships in the real world often vary with time, and can rarely be labeled with a single formula or function.

Launch

Read or tell the story of Sascha's bicycle ride to the class. Discuss what information is given and how it can be used to find the total distance Sascha traveled, or let each group make sense of the story for themselves. Whichever way you launch the problem, be sure students understand what the questions are asking, especially parts C and D. If your students are likely to have trouble with the fractional times, you may need to help them begin by constructing a table of the data and filling in the first two 5-minute intervals as a group.

Speed	45 mph	45 mph	30 mph	25 mph	25 mph	25 mph
Time interval	5 min	5 min	5 min	5 min	5 min	5 min
Elapsed time	5 min	10 min	15 min	20 min	25 min	30 min
Distance for interval	$\frac{5}{60} \times 45 =$ $3\frac{3}{4}$ mi	$\frac{5}{60} \times 45 =$ $3\frac{3}{4}$ mi	$\frac{5}{60} \times 30 =$ $2\frac{1}{2}$ mi	$\frac{5}{60} \times 25 =$ $2\frac{1}{12}$ mi	$\frac{5}{60} \times 25 =$ $2\frac{1}{12}$ mi	$\frac{5}{60} \times 25 =$ $2\frac{1}{12}$ mi
Total distance	$3\frac{3}{4}$ mi	$7\frac{1}{2}$ mi	10 mi	$12\frac{1}{12}$ mi	$14\frac{2}{12}$ mi	$16\frac{3}{12}$ mi

Explore

Have students work on the problem and follow-up in groups of two to four. Students first make a graph showing how the distance Sascha traveled changed over time.

As groups work on part D, look for students demonstrating naive ideas about how to find the constant speed needed to match Sascha's performance. For example, if students have averaged Sascha's speeds, ask:

> How far would that speed take you in 1 hour?

If groups cannot find a way to get started, ask them to focus on exactly what they know about Sascha's trip. (He traveled for an hour. He rode 26.25 miles.) Then, ask the group to tell you in their own words what part D is asking them to figure out.

You may want to distribute blank transparent grids to groups with particularly good graphs for sharing in the summary.

Summarize

Give groups a chance to share their answers and their strategies. Have them explain how they found the numbers needed to construct their graphs. Ask questions to help the class analyze exactly what the graph shows.

> How does the graph reflect the change in speed each time Sascha decreased his speed?

> Are the distances you computed for Sascha exact or approximate? Why?

For the Teacher: Piecewise Linear Graphs

Since Sascha's rate of speed changed, the graph of the distance he traveled over time is not linear, but it is constructed of linear parts—sometimes called *piecewise linear.* Figuring out what constant speed another person would have to travel to cover the same distance in the same time is an interesting problem, because the answer is not the average of all of Sascha's speeds. There are *two* quantities involved—that is, a rate—and finding the average speed must account for both distance and time.

Discuss the follow-up question. Students have been dealing with situations in which the rate of change is constant. Trying to write an equation to predict Sascha's distance from the amount of time he has been riding raises the issue of growth that is linear in parts but alters its rate of change over time. An equation can be written for each segment of the graph along which the speed is constant, but no single equation would be valid throughout the hour that Sascha rode.

For the Teacher: Rules for Piecewise Graphs

To write a rule at each speed, you would need to give the times for which each rule would be valid. However, even this would not tell you total distance traveled, unless the rule for a segment included a term that added on the total so far. For example, from 0 to 10 minutes, the rule would be $d = \frac{45}{60}t$ (where $\frac{45}{60}$ is the rate in miles per minute, and the time is in minutes). From 10 to 15 minutes, the rule would be $d = \frac{30}{60}t + 7.5$.

4.4 • Buying Beads

This straightforward problem offers you an opportunity to make an informal assessment of the sense students are making of rates, unit rates, and the relationship between unit rates and rules. It also gives students who are still struggling a chance to think about the ideas again in a very simple context.

Launch

As a class, discuss the crafts store owner's bead advertisement.

Explore

Have students work in pairs on the problem and follow-up. As they write rules to predict the cost of any number of beads of a particular kind, look for students who are exhibiting good understanding. Ask questions to help them to make their ideas more explicit.

How much would 10 spheres cost? *(6¢)* 5 spheres? *(3¢)* 1 sphere? $(\frac{3}{5}¢)$

How can you use this unit rate fraction—cost per sphere—to write a rule to predict the bill for a given number of spheres? $(c = \frac{3}{5}x)$

Summarize

If your students seem to be doing well with these ideas, this can be a short summary. If they need a little more exposure, take the time to let them explain how they thought about the problem and what they did to find a solution.

When students seem comfortable, offer another problem as a quick check. For example:

> Suppose Christen sees a tetrahedral-shaped bead that she likes. They cost 15¢ for 9 beads. Write a rule relating the cost of the tetrahedral beads to the number of beads. $(c = \frac{15}{9}x)$

Discuss the follow-up questions.

> For spherical beads, the two unit rates are $\frac{3}{5}¢$ per sphere and $\frac{5}{3}$ spheres per cent. If I have 20 cents, which ratio most efficiently helps me to find how many spheres I can buy? $(\frac{5}{3} \times 20$ rather than $20 \div \frac{3}{5})$

Additional Answers

Answers to Problem 4.2

B.	Gallons of gas	0	1	2	3	4	5	6	7	8
	Miles in Madeline's car	0	30.5	61.0	91.5	122.0	152.5	183.0	213.5	244.0
	Miles in Luis's car	0	29.2	58.4	87.6	116.8	146.0	175.2	204.4	233.6

D.	Gallons of gas	9.5	15.5	19	23.8	100	125	150
	Miles in Madeline's car	289.8	472.8	579.5	725.9	3050.0	3812.5	4575.0
	Miles in Luis's car	277.4	452.6	554.8	695.0	2920.0	3650.0	4380.0

Answers to Problem 4.2 Follow-Up

1.

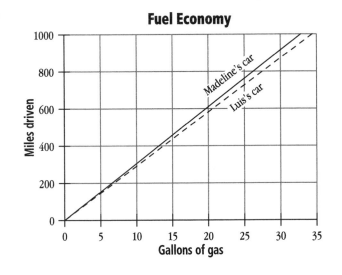

2. Both lines are straight and pass through (0, 0). The line for Madeline's car is slightly steeper, which means that her car goes a bit farther on a gallon of gas.

3. The difference between the graphs results from the two cars' different miles-per-gallon unit rate.

Answers to Problem 4.3

A.

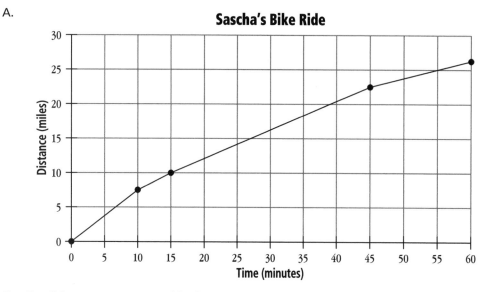

Sascha's Bike Ride

C. Possible answers: A rate table shows that you would have to ride just over 2 h to travel 26.25 mi.

Time (h)	1	2	3
Distance (mi)	13	26	39

Or, you would have to travel 26.25 mi ÷ 13 mph = 2.02 h.

ACE Answers

Applications

2b.

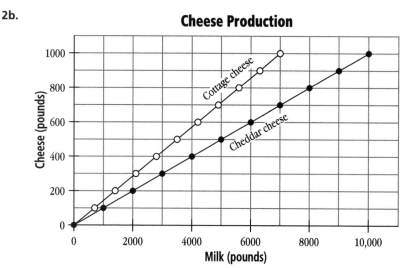

Cheese Production

Mathematical Reflections

2. When there are two or more of the same basic kind of rates in a problem, finding a unit rate makes the comparison easy. For example, suppose we can buy packages of crackers at 6 for $5.00, 8 for $7.50, or 3 for $2.25. Which is the best buy? The related unit rates are 84¢, 94¢, and 75¢ per package. Now the best buy is clear. We could also compare the original rates, scaling up until we have an equal number of packages.

Packages	6	12	18	24
Cost ($)	5.00	10.00	15.00	20.00

Packages	8	16	24
Cost ($)	7.50	15.00	22.50

Packages	3	6	9	12	15	18	21	24
Cost ($)	2.25	4.50	6.75	9.00	11.25	13.50	15.75	18.00

4. To make a table for this example, we assume that we can buy any number of packages and get the price per package. One package costs 84¢, so we multiply by the number of packages to fill in the table.

Packages	1	2	3	4	5
Cost ($)	0.84	1.68	2.52	3.36	4.20

The table can be used to plot points for a graph by putting one variable on each axis.

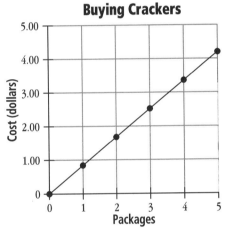

Buying Crackers

Estimating Populations and Population Densities

In Investigation 5, students apply the strategies they have learned about using ratios and scaling to estimate the size of populations that are difficult to count or inaccessible. They explore techniques for estimating wildlife populations and scaling up from aerial photographs to estimate crowd size.

The first two problems involve estimating the size of a population. In Problem 5.1, Estimating the Size of a Crowd, students simulate the estimation of the size of a large crowd at a rally. Problem 5.2, Estimating a Deer Population, is based on the classic capture-tag-recapture technique for counting wildlife populations. Students simulate the technique by taking and analyzing samples from a container of beans.

The remaining problems focus on population density. In Problem 5.3, Finding Population Densities, students investigate the areas and population densities of the nine geographical regions used to organize U.S. census data. In Problem 5.4, Comparing the Dakotas, they compute the population densities of the two states and then attempt to "equalize" them by moving people from one state to the other. Problem 5.5, Predicting Traffic Jams, introduces students to the idea of traffic density. Students review data on three cities and decide which would most likely have traffic jams.

Mathematical and Problem-Solving Goals

- *To use geometric scaling to estimate population counts*

- *To apply proportional reasoning to situations in which capture-tag-recapture methods are appropriate for estimating population counts*

- *To use ratios and scaling up or down (finding equivalent ratios) to find the missing value in a proportion*

- *To use rates to describe population and traffic density (space per person or car)*

Materials		
Problem	**For students**	**For the teacher**
All	Graphing calculators	Transparencies 5.1 to 5.5 (optional)
5.1	Transparencies of centimeter and inch grid paper (about 1 per group)	News article that reports an estimate of crowd size (optional)
5.2	Containers (large enough so students can mix the contents) of 300–800 white beans, with lid (1 per group); markers (1 per group); scoops for sampling (optional; 1 per group)	

Estimating the Size of a Crowd

Grouping:
groups of 2 or 3

Launch

- Introduce the topic of estimating crowd size and the challenge of estimating the number of people in the simulated photograph.

Explore

- As groups work on the problem and follow-up, remind them to be prepared to explain their methods.

- Have transparent grids available for groups who want to use them.

Summarize

- As groups share their estimates and their reasoning, make a list of their estimates.

- At the projector, demonstrate counting the data in a small area and using ratios to estimate the total. *(optional)*

- Talk about how this method may lead to a poor estimate.

Assignment Choices

ACE questions 3, 10, and unassigned choices from earlier problems

---

INVESTIGATION

Estimating Populations and Population Densities

Since counting is one of the first mathematics skills you learned, you might expect solving a counting problem to be easy. However, sometimes counting things can get complicated.

> ### Think about this!
>
> **H**ow would you count the number of people attending a Fourth of July fireworks show or a human-rights rally on the mall of our nation's capital?
>
> How would you count the number of deer in a forest, the number of fish in a stream, or the number of bees in a hive?
>
> Share your ideas about these problems with your class. Be sure to discuss the factors that make the counting in each situation difficult.

 Estimating the Size of a Crowd

News reports often give estimates of the sizes of crowds at political rallies, parades, and festivals. In 1994, television reporters announced that 350,000 people had attended a Fourth of July concert and fireworks display in front of the Capitol in Washington, D.C. How do you think this estimate was made? Do you think someone actually counted each individual in the crowd?

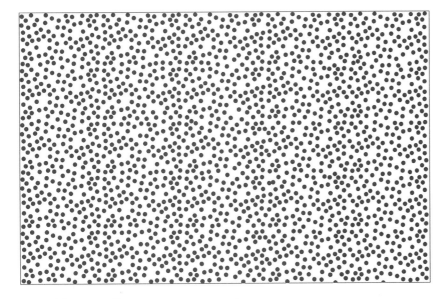

Problem 5.1

Sometimes the size of a crowd is estimated from aerial photographs. Imagine that the illustration below is an aerial photograph of a crowd at a rally. Each dot represents one person.

Estimate how many people attended the rally. Explain the method you used to arrive at your answer.

■ Problem 5.1 Follow-Up

In your group, discuss ways your method might lead to a poor estimate of the crowd size.

Answer to Problem 5.1

Estimates will vary, depending on how students tackle the problem. Estimates on the order of 1500 to 2500 people are reasonable.

Answer to Problem 5.1 Follow-Up

Some of the reasons students' methods may lead to a poor estimate of crowd size are that crowds are not always evenly dispersed, that the sample taken may not be representative, that errors may be made in counting or computation, that the photograph of a crowd may not be clear, and that crowds may change as people wander in and out.

Estimating a Deer Population

At a Glance

**Grouping:
small groups**

Launch

- Ask students how estimates of large, mobile populations might be made.

- Review the bean simulation of the capture-tag-recapture method.

Explore

- As groups explore the bean simulation, ask questions to keep them focused.

- Allow groups to use a variety of strategies to estimate the number of beans.

Summarize

- Guide a discussion of the groups' findings and methods of conducting the experiment.

- Talk about how the method could lead to a poor estimate.

Assignment Choices

ACE questions 1, 2, 4, 13, 14, and unassigned choices from earlier problems

5.2 Estimating a Deer Population

In states with large populations of white-tailed deer, like Michigan, biologists in the Department of Natural Resources are asked to make estimates of deer populations. The estimates are used to set hunting seasons and regulations. But how is it possible to count all the deer in Michigan—or even in a small part of the state?

One method biologists use to count animal populations is the *capture-tag-recapture* method. You can simulate this method by using a jar or box filled with white beans. Imagine that each bean is a deer in the upper peninsula of Michigan. Your job is to estimate the number of deer without actually counting them all.

Problem 5.2

Your group will need a container with a lid and a large number of white beans. Work with your group to perform this experiment.

- Remove exactly 100 beans from the container, and mark them with a pen or marker.

- Put the marked beans back into the container, and shake or mix them with the unmarked beans.

- Without looking at the beans, scoop out a handful of about 30 beans. Record the numbers of marked and unmarked beans in this sample. Return the sample to the jar, and mix the beans together again.

- Repeat this scoop-and-count procedure four more times. In each case, record the number of marked and unmarked beans.

A. Study the data you collected. Use the data to estimate the number of beans in your container. Explain how you made your estimate.

B. Based on what you have learned from this experiment, how do you think biologists count deer populations?

■ Problem 5.2 Follow-Up

In your group, discuss ways in which this method might give a poor estimate of the actual number of deer in a population. Record your ideas.

Answers to Problem 5.2

See page 64h.

Answer to Problem 5.2 Follow-Up

There are many reasons why this method might lead to a poor estimate of a live population. The tagged deer might not return to the area where they were captured. Tagged deer might become more—or less—wary of recapture. The tagged animals may not have been taken from areas representative of the population. As in the crowd situation, the tagged deer may not be distributed evenly within the area so that the sampling does not match the distribution or does not take into account how the herd moves during the day.

Finding Population Densities

Sometimes a simple count does not tell you the whole story. To understand some situations, you need to count or measure two or more things and determine how the measures or counts are related. For example, suppose you are interested in how crowded a city, state, country, or other geographic region is. It is not enough to consider the number of people in the region. You must also consider the amount of available land.

Think about this!

When we reach the year 2000, there will be over 6 billion people living on our planet. But we are not evenly distributed over the 58 million square miles that make up the seven continents; some cities, states, and countries are much more crowded than others.

What do you think are the most and least crowded places on earth? How could you use land area and population data to test your ideas?

Below is a map of the United States divided into the nine regions used in reporting data from the census.

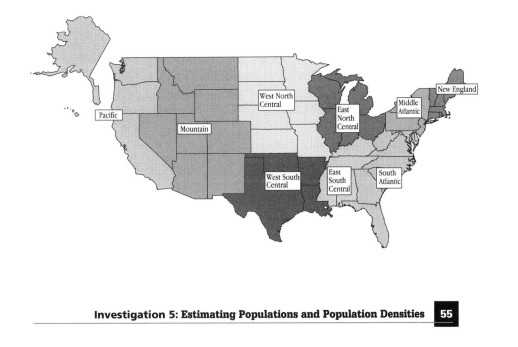

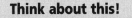

Investigation 5: Estimating Populations and Population Densities **55**

Finding Population Densities

At a Glance

Grouping: pairs

Launch

- Conduct an activity, such as packing students into 1 square meter, to demonstrate the concept of population density. *(optional)*

- Discuss the two ways to express population density: people per unit of area and area per person.

Explore

- Ask each pair to find the density of their region and one other region.

- Have pairs share their data and then do parts C and D.

Summarize

- Ask students to share their findings and to talk about their methods.

- Discuss possible reasons for the differences in population density among the regions.

Assignment Choices

ACE questions 5, 7, 8, and unassigned choices from earlier problems

This table shows the 1994 population and land area for the nine census regions.

Region	Population	Area (square miles)
New England	13,270,000	62,811
Middle Atlantic	38,125,000	99,463
South Atlantic	46,398,000	266,221
East North Central	43,184,000	243,539
East South Central	15,890,000	178,615
West North Central	18,210,000	507,981
West South Central	28,404,000	426,234
Mountain	15,214,000	856,121
Pacific	41,645,000	895,353

Source: *Statistical Abstract of the United States 1995.* Published by the Bureau of the Census, Washington, D.C., pp. 28 and 225.

Problem 5.3

The "crowdedness" of a region is commonly reported by giving the number of people (or animals or plants) per unit of area. This rate is called the **population density** of the region.

A. What is the population density of the census region in which your school is located?

B. Divide the remaining eight census regions among the groups in your class. Find the population density of the region you are assigned. Share your group's results with the rest of the class, so that every group has data for all nine regions.

C. Order the regions from least crowded to most crowded.

D. Compare the population density of the region in which you live to the population density of each neighboring region. Write complete sentences explaining which regions you are comparing and describing how their population densities compare.

 Problem 5.3 Follow-Up

What do you think accounts for the differences in population densities among the regions? In other words, why do you think some areas are densely populated and others are more sparsely populated?

Answers to Problem 5.3

See page 64i.

Answer to Problem 5.3 Follow-Up

See the Summarize section for several reasons for the differences in population densities.

Comparing the Dakotas

5.4 Comparing the Dakotas

South Dakota and North Dakota rank 45 and 47 in population of all the states in the United States. South Dakota has 721,000 people in 75,896 square miles of land, and North Dakota has 638,000 people in 68,994 square miles of land.

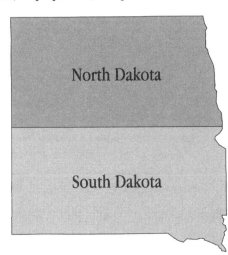

Problem 5.4

A. Which state, North Dakota or South Dakota, has the greater population density?

B. How many citizens of one state would have to move to the other state to make the population densities in the two states equal? Explain how you arrived at your answer.

▓ Problem 5.4 Follow-Up

Find the population density of your state. How does it compare to the population densities of North and South Dakota?

Launch

- Ask students to do part A individually as a quick check of their understanding.

- Talk about their ideas in a class discussion.

- Have groups discuss part B.

Explore

- Encourage groups having trouble to start by making a reasonable guess.

Summarize

- As a class, share and discuss strategies for solving the problem.

- Use the follow-up as a check on students' understanding (they will need their state's area in square miles).

Answers to Problem 5.4

A. South Dakota has the greater population density.

B. Approximately 9164 people would need to move from South Dakota to North Dakota to make the density in each state the same. (See the Summarize section for two examples of how this might be calculated.)

Answer to Problem 5.4 Follow-Up

Answers will vary.

Assignment Choices

ACE questions 6, 12, and unassigned choices from earlier problems

5.5

Predicting Traffic Jams

***Grouping:
small groups***

Launch

- Engage the class in a discussion about traffic and traffic jams.

- Read or explain the data about the three cities.

Explore

- Have groups of two or three find the two kinds of rates for each city and compare them.

- As you circulate, ask clarifying questions and remind students to label their results.

Summarize

- Talk about how groups solved the problem.

- Highlight efficient strategies that were used.

- Discuss the follow-up questions about traffic congestion.

You have probably been in a traffic jam or two. What kinds of things cause traffic jams? How can you predict where traffic jams are likely to occur?

One way to identify places where traffic jams are likely is by calculating traffic densities. Hong Kong is reported to have the highest traffic density in the world. In 1992, there were 418 registered cars and trucks per mile of road, or about 12.63 feet per registered vehicle! (Source: *Guinness Book of Records 1994.* Ed. Peter Matthews. New York: Bantam Books, 1994, p. 318.)

> ### Problem 5.5
>
> **A.** The city of Ole has 450,237 registered vehicles for 3000 miles of road. What is the traffic density of Ole? Calculate the number of vehicles per mile of road and the number of feet of road per vehicle.
>
> **B.** The city of Driftwood Bay has 396 registered vehicles for 10 miles of road. What is the traffic density of Driftwood Bay? Calculate the number of vehicles per mile of road and the number of feet of road per vehicle.
>
> **C.** Which of the three cities—Hong Kong, Ole, or Driftwood Bay—do you think is most likely to have traffic jams? Explain your answer.
>
> **D.** Which of the three cities do you think is least likely to have traffic jams? Explain your answer.

■ Problem 5.5 Follow-Up

1. Other than traffic density, what factors might affect the likelihood of traffic jams?

2. A typical four-passenger car is about 13 feet long. Compare this statistic to the amount of road per mile in Hong Kong. What does this say about traffic in Hong Kong? What might Hong Kong do if this situation gets worse?

Assignment Choices

ACE questions 9, 11, and unassigned choices from earlier problems

Answers to Problem 5.5

A. The traffic density of Ole is $\frac{450,237}{3000}$ = 150.1 vehicles per mi. The amount of road per vehicle is $\frac{3000}{450,237}$ = 0.006663 mi per vehicle or 35.18 ft per vehicle.

B. Driftwood Bay has a traffic density of $\frac{396}{10}$ = 39.6 vehicles per mi. The amount of road per vehicle is $\frac{10}{396}$ = 0.02525 mi per vehicle or 133.3 ft per vehicle.

C. See page 64i.

D. Driftwood Bay is the least likely to have a traffic jam of the three cities, because it has the most feet of road per vehicle.

Answers to Problem 5.5 Follow-Up

See the Summarize section for several factors other than traffic density that might affect the likelihood of traffic jams and for ideas about how to reduce traffic congestion.

As you work on these ACE questions, use your calculator whenever you need it.

Applications

1. Yung-nan wants to estimate the number of beans in a jar. She took out a sample of 150 beans, marked them, returned them to the jar, and mixed them with the unmarked beans. She then gathered some data by taking samples. Use her data to predict the number of beans in the jar.

Sample 1
Number of marked beans: 2
Beans in sample: 25

Sample 3
Number of marked beans: 23
Beans in sample: 150

Sample 2
Number of marked beans: 10
Beans in sample: 75

Sample 4
Number of marked beans: 38
Beans in sample: 250

2. Describe a method for estimating (not counting!) the blades of grass on a football field.

3. After testing many samples, an electric company determined that approximately 2 of every 1000 light bulbs on the market are defective. Americans buy over a billion light bulbs every year. Estimate how many of these bulbs are defective.

Answers

Applications

1. Possible answers: Based on the total of the four samples, around $\frac{73}{500}$ = 15% of the beans in the jar are marked, so there are about 150 ÷ 0.15 = 1000 beans in the jar. Or, by scaling up the ratio of marked beans in the jar to marked beans in the largest sample, 150 ÷ 38 = approximately 4, so the total number of beans is about 4 × 250 = 1000.

2. Possible answer: We could look at a small region of the field, count the number of blades in that region, and multiply the number of regions of this size in the football field by our count.

3. The rate of defective bulbs is approximately $\frac{2}{1000} = \frac{1}{500}$. Therefore, more than $\frac{1}{500} \times$ 1,000,000,000 = 2,000,000 are defective per year.

Investigation 5

4a. For every 2 tagged puffins, there are actually about 50 puffins in the population. Since 20 puffins in the population are tagged, there are about 500 puffins on the island.

4b. Possible answer: For this estimate to be accurate, the tagged puffins must have evenly mixed throughout the island with the untagged puffins. Also, the population on the island must have remained fairly stable from summer to summer.

4. Angela Krebs, a biologist, spends summers on an island off the coast of Alaska. For several summers she studied the puffin, a black-and-white seabird with a flat, brightly colored bill. Two summers ago, Angela trapped 20 puffins, then tagged and released them. This past summer, she trapped 50 puffins and found that 2 of them were tagged. She used this information to estimate the total puffin population on the island.

a. Using Angela's findings, estimate the number of puffins on the island. Explain how you made your estimate.

b. How confident are you that your estimate is accurate? Explain your answer.

In 5–8, use the data in the following table.

Population and Land Area of Selected States

State	Population	Area (square miles)
California	31,431,000	155,973
Connecticut	3,275,000	4845
New Hampshire	1,137,000	8969
North Dakota	638,000	68,994
South Dakota	721,000	75,896
Vermont	580,000	9249
Wyoming	476,000	97,105

Source: *Statistical Abstract of the United States 1995.* Published by the Bureau of the Census, Washington, D.C., pp. 28 and 225.

5. a. Find the population density of each state in the table.

    b. Which state has the highest population density?

    c. Which state has the lowest population density?

6. How many people would have to move from Connecticut to Wyoming to make the population densities in the two states the same? Explain.

7. How many times would the land area of Connecticut fit into the land area of Wyoming? Explain.

8. How many times greater is the population of Connecticut than the population of Wyoming? Explain.

9. The city of Canton has three parks: Flyaway Park has an area of 5000 m², Golden Park has an area of 7235 m², and Pine Park has an area of 3060 m².

    a. At 2 P.M. last Saturday, 400 children were playing in Flyaway Park, 630 were in Golden Park, and 255 were in Pine Park. Rank the parks from least crowded to most crowded. Explain how you got your answer.

    b. Oak Park is located in the suburbs of Canton. It has area of 5240 m². At 2 P.M. last Saturday, 462 children were playing in Oak Park. How crowded was Oak Park at this time compared to Flyaway, Golden, and Pine?

Connections

10. At Raccoon Middle School, Ms. Picadello's students conducted a class survey about their favorite rock bands. Of the 35 students in the class, 20 picked the Nerds, 8 picked the Promise, and 7 picked Willie and the Wonders.

    a. If you randomly selected 10 students in the halls of Raccoon Middle School and asked what their favorite rock band was, would you expect the same ratio as in Ms. Picadello's class? Why or why not?

    b. Would you expect the same ratio if you asked 10 middle-school students from another state the same question? Why or why not?

5a. See below left.

5b. Connecticut

5c. Wyoming

6. See below left.

7. The land area of Connecticut would fit into the land area of Wyoming about 97,105 ÷ 4845 = 20 times.

8. The population of Connecticut is about 3,275,000 ÷ 476,000 = 6.9 times the population of Wyoming.

9a. From least to most crowded, the parks are Flyaway Park (5000 ÷ 400 = 12.5 m² per child), Pine Park (3060 ÷ 255 = 12.0 m² per child), and Golden Park (7235 ÷ 630 = 11.5 m² per child).

9b. With 5240 ÷ 462 = 11.3 m² per child, Oak Park was more crowded than the other three parks.

Connections

10a. Ms. Picadello's class may not be representative of the entire school, so these ratios may not be the same. Also, a sample of only 10 students is quite small and probably would not capture the diversity of the school.

10b. These ratios would probably not be the same, since local tastes often differ.

5a.

State	Population density (people per mi²)
California	31,431,000 ÷ 155,973 = 201.5
Connecticut	3,275,000 ÷ 4845 = 676.0
New Hampshire	1,137,000 ÷ 8969 = 126.8
North Dakota	638,000 ÷ 68,994 = 9.2
South Dakota	721,000 ÷ 75,896 = 9.5
Vermont	580,000 ÷ 9249 = 62.7
Wyoming	476,000 ÷ 97,105 = 4.9

6. Possible answer: By combining the data for the two states, we get an overall population density of $\frac{3,751,000}{101,950}$ = 36.8 people per mi². To give Wyoming this population density, about 97,105 × 36.8 = 3,573,464 people would have to live in Wyoming. This means that about 3,573,464 − 476,000 = 3,097,464 people would have to move from Connecticut to Wyoming for the states to have equal population densities.

11a. Shanda has made $\frac{500}{1000}$ or 50%, and Michi has made $\frac{175}{350}$ or 50%, so they have the same free-throw averages.

11b. The new averages would be $\frac{510}{1010}$ or 50.5% for Shanda and $\frac{185}{360}$ or 51.4% for Michi. Michi's average increased more than Shanda's, but both increased only slightly.

12a. This question is designed to get students to think back to their work on similarity. They might suggest using a rubber-band stretcher to draw the new map, projecting the original on an overhead projector and tracing the image, or using a transparent grid to find coordinates for locations on the original and drawing the image by using the rule $(2x, 2y)$.

12b. The new scale would be about 1 in = 300 mi.

13. See page 64j.

---

11. Shanda and Michi play a lot of basketball, and they keep a record of their free-throw attempts in practices and games. Shanda has made 500 of 1000 free-throw attempts in the last month, and Michi has made 175 of 350.

a. Compare Shanda's and Michi's free-throw shooting.

b. How would their success rates change if they each make their next 10 free-throw attempts? Are you surprised at the results? Why or why not?

12. The map on page 55 has a scale of about 1 inch = 600 miles. (Alaska and Hawaii are not drawn to this scale.) Excluding Alaska and Hawaii, the map is about 5 inches wide and 2.5 inches high.

a. How could you draw a version of the map that is about 10 inches by 5 inches?

b. What would the scale of your enlarged map be?

13. A jar contains 150 marked beans. Scott took several samples from the jar and got these results:

Beans in sample	25	50	75	100	150	200	250
Marked beans	3	12	13	17	27	38	52
Percent marked beans	12%						

a. Copy the table, and complete the last row to show the percent of marked beans in each sample.

b. Graph the (beans in sample, marked beans) data. Describe the pattern of data points in your graph. What does the pattern tell you about the relationship between the number of beans in a sample and the number of marked beans you can expect to find in the sample?

c. Make a graph of the (beans in sample, percent marked beans) data. Describe the pattern of data points in your graph. What does the pattern tell you about the relationship between the number of beans in a sample and the percent of marked beans you can expect to find in the sample?

Extensions

14. Conduct an experiment in your neighborhood or school to help you predict the number of people in the United States who are left-handed. Make the assumption that your neighborhood or school is representative of the general population in left-handedness. Assume that the population of the United States is about 260 million. Describe your experiment and the results you predict for the population of the United States.

14. Answers will vary. If it is not feasible for students to sample from their neighborhood or the entire school, they could look at the number of their classmates who are left-handed.

Possible Answers

1a. See page 64k.

1b. We can think of 30% as 30 to 100, so we need to find an equivalent ratio of the form 40 to *what*. Since 40 is 1.33 times greater than 30, we need to scale 100 by 1.33. This gives about 133 fish.

2. In every density problem, we needed to know a measure of space and a measure of things (like people or cars) filling that space. To find the population density, we divided one of the quantities by the other.

3a. Either a count of tagged deer and the total number of deer that were tagged, or a count of the deer in one representative area, the measure of the area, and the measure of the total wildlife area.

3b. A count of the trees in one area of the forest, the measure of that area, and the measure of the area of the entire forest.

4. The comparison that most resembles population-density comparisons is part b, miles per gallon, because it is a unit rate.

In this investigation, you used sampling and ratios to estimate the size of a population. You also used the idea of population density to describe and compare the "crowdedness" of geographic regions and roads. These questions will help you summarize what you have learned:

1. For each situation, explain how you could use the given information to estimate the total population of fish in the pond. Be sure to include any assumptions you make.

   a. Biologists caught 25 fish in a net, tagged them, and returned them to the pond. In a later catch of 20 fish, 3 had tags.

   b. Park officials tagged and released 40 fish. They kept records of the fish caught over the next month and found that 30% had tags.

2. In the problems in this investigation, what data did you need to find the densities of populations?

3. **a.** What data would you need to estimate the density of deer in a wildlife area?

   b. What data would you need to estimate the density of trees in a forest?

4. Which of the following comparison statements is most like the population-density comparisons? Explain your reasoning.

   a. People prefer Bolda Cola to Cola Nola by a ratio of 3 to 2.

   b. Mary's car gets 30.5 miles per gallon of gas.

   c. The population of California is 28,156,000 greater than the population of Connecticut.

   Think about your answers to these questions, discuss your ideas with other students and your teacher, and then write a summary of your findings in your journal.

Tips for the Linguistically Diverse Classroom

Original Rebus The Original Rebus technique is described in detail in *Getting to Know Connected Mathematics*. Students make a copy of the text before it is discussed. During the discussion, they generate their own rebuses for words they do not understand; the words are made comprehensible through pictures, objects, or demonstrations. Example: Question 1a—Key phrases for which students might make rebuses are *fish* (outlines of fish), *net* (crisscrossed lines over the fish), *tagged them* (tags with check marks), *returned them to the pond* (stick figures dropping fish into water).

TEACHING THE INVESTIGATION

5.1 • Estimating the Size of a Crowd

In this problem, students will develop strategies for estimating the size of a crowd pictured in an aerial photograph.

Launch

Introduce the topic by asking students whether they have ever read or heard about estimates of crowd size. You might look for an article to share with the class in which the crowd size at some event is given.

> How do you think such estimates can be made?

After taking a few ideas from the class, display Transparency 5.1, or refer students to the simulated crowd photograph in the student edition.

> Your challenge is to figure out a way to make a good estimate of the size of the crowd represented by the dots in this illustration.

Explore

Have students work in groups of two or three to make their estimates. Remind them to be prepared to explain their estimation method.

Have transparencies of centimeter and inch grids available for students to use. Allow groups to try any method they devise, but some may ask for grids. If some groups are having a hard time coming up with a method for estimating the number of dots, you could point out that the grids are available.

When groups have made their estimates, ask them to discuss the follow-up.

Summarize

The key to this problem is to get students to explain their reasoning. Have groups share how they thought about the problem. Record their crowd estimates for the class to examine. Point out the range of estimates.

> What might influence the variation we see in these estimates?

> How might the data from all the groups be used to make an even better estimate?

Students will probably suggest computing a mean or median of the groups' estimates. Ask students why this is a reasonable strategy for finding a good estimate for the population, then follow through with the suggestion.

If no group has thought of counting the number of people (dots) in a small area and using the ratio of the small area to the whole area to estimate the total population, you might demonstrate this method at the overhead projector using a transparent grid.

What do you think about this method? Does it give an estimate that is similar to the other methods used by the class?

Is taking one sample enough, or should we take more than one sample and average (or *aggregate*) the data to estimate the size of the crowd?

Taking one sample might lead to a poor estimate of crowd size with live populations. For instance, a crowd may not be evenly dispersed in the area. At a concert, the crowd near the stage may be denser than the crowd further from the stage. If sampling is done on an area that is not very representative of the whole crowd, an overestimate or underestimate will result.

5.2 • Estimating a Deer Population

In this problem, students conduct an experiment to simulate counting the deer in the upper peninsula of Michigan. If you know of a more appropriate local example, you may want to substitute it. For example: "The Department of Natural Resources manages the fish population in the Bay and sets catch limits to protect certain species of fish. How do they measure the size of each fish species' population?"

Launch

Introduce the topic by asking about techniques for estimating the size of populations that won't line up for counting.

How do wildlife officials determine how many eagles there are in the United States?

How do environmentalists decide whether an animal or plant should be on the endangered species list?

For the Teacher: Solving by Proportions

In this problem, students can construct a proportion by setting the ratio of marked beans in the container to the entire population equal to the ratio of marked beans in a drawn sample. While both this problem and Problem 5.1 can be posed in classic $\frac{a}{b} = \frac{x}{d}$ or $\frac{a}{b} = \frac{c}{x}$ form, they are often solved in a variety of other ways. We have not outlined the traditional proportion method, but have continued to encourage students to think about the problems in whatever ways make the most sense to them.

Review the steps of the bean experiment. You may want to demonstrate the experiment with a small container of beans:

■ Take a sample and mark them. Remember how many you marked!

■ Return the marked beans to the container. Ask students what to do now.

■ Mix the marked and unmarked beans together. Show the container, and ask students how the procedure might help to estimate the total number of beans in the container.

■ Take a new sample, and count the marked and unmarked beans. Ask students what they now know.

What students need to recognize is that they know (1) the number of marked beans in the whole population and (2) the number of marked beans in the sample.

> How can you use what you know about making comparisons with ratios to estimate the number of beans in the whole population?

Ask students to think about how the experiment models what really happens when the capture-tag-recapture method is used to estimate the number of deer in a large forest. Some factors that must be considered are tagging deer from several places in the area of concern, taking a sufficient sample for tagging, allowing the tagged animals time to mix thoroughly with the population, and taking the final samples from several places in the area.

When students understand the experiment and how it relates to counting animals in a large population, give each group of three or four a container of beans, a marker, and, optionally, a small scoop for taking samples from the container.

Explore

Have groups work on the problem and then talk about the follow-up. As you circulate, ask questions to help keep the groups focused.

> How are you mixing the beans? How are you keeping track of what you know?

> How does the number of samples you have taken affect your estimate?

Students may use a variety of strategies to reason about how to estimate the size of the population (the number of beans in the container). At this point, we are interested in the varied strategies they invent, not in simply imposing "the proportion strategy."

Summarize

Once groups have analyzed their data, have them report how they conducted the experiment and what they found. Guide the discussion with questions such as the following:

> Why did you mix all the beans after you added the marked sample of beans? How would a Natural Resources ranger "stir" the deer?

Why is it a good idea to take several samples before deciding what to use for the ratio of marked beans to unmarked beans in the sample?

Explain exactly how you used the information from your various counts to make your estimate of the total number of beans in the container.

As the number of samples you took increased, what change occurred in the ratio of marked beans to unmarked beans?

If students aggregated their data, they should notice that the more samples they took, the more the ratio of marked to unmarked beans stabilized.

Ask groups to share their ideas about how the capture-tag-recapture method might lead to a poor estimate of a population of deer in the wild.

5.3 • Finding Population Densities

Your students may have had very little experience with population density. The activities proposed here have value in other fields where density (the number of people per unit of area or the amount of area per person) is an important concept.

Launch

If your students need more exposure to the concept of population density, you may choose to conduct the following introductory activity. Mark off a square, 2 yards by 2 yards, and ask:

If we have an area of 4 square yards and we put 8 students in that area, how many students will there be per square yard? How are you reasoning about this?

The question focuses on the *number of students per square yard*. Another way of getting at this idea is to ask:

What is the mean number of students in each square yard?

Have 8 students arrange themselves in the 4-square-yard space. You may want to ask them to reposition themselves several times, each time returning to the original question. There are 2 students per square yard no matter how the students arrange themselves.

What if there were 15 students in our square? What would the new mean number of students in each square yard be? What if we had 3 students in our square?

Explain that we are describing the *population density* when we answer questions like these.

Now, tell me the two rates that make sense in describing the density of a population in a given area—for example, the 8 students in the 4 square yards of area.

Help students see that *people per unit of area* and *area per person* are both reasonable ways to describe population density. In the example, we can say that there are 2 students per square yard or $\frac{1}{2}$ of a square yard per person.

> Suppose we wanted to determine the population density of our state. What would we need to know? *(the state's area and population)*
>
> What measures for area may be more appropriate than square yards when we are looking at the area of a state?

Square miles, square kilometers, and acres (1 square mile = 640 acres) are all more appropriate units than square yards. Help students develop an understanding of the size of 1 square mile in relation to their work with square yards: 1 mile = 5280 feet = 1760 yards, so 1 square mile = 3,097,600 square yards. An American football field is about 100 yards by 55 yards, or 5500 square yards; it would take about 563 football fields to make a square mile.

Display Transparency 5.3A, or refer students to the map and the table of data in the student edition. Help them to identify the regions on the map referred to in the table.

Explore

Challenge students to work in pairs to find the population density of the census region in which the school is located. Assign each pair one other region as well; pairs will need to share their data before doing parts C and D.

You may want pairs to record and label their estimates on the board, which will give you a way to check their accuracy and help you to see which pairs have the right idea and which may need assistance.

Students may need some help devising strategies for determining population densities for the regions. Some may compute people per square mile; others may compute square miles per person. Measures of population density are usually given in people per square mile (or acre). Have the class agree to use population per unit of area as the measure for parts C and D.

When all pairs have reported their estimates, bring the class together to inspect and clean up the data.

> Does the data for each region seem reasonable based on the population and area of each region?

Reach an agreement on what measures to use, and ask each pair to record those population densities for use in parts C and D.

Summarize

Have students talk about what they found and how they made their decisions. If there are disagreements about which regions touch your school's region, help the class to resolve them. For any population density given, ask what the numbers mean. Focus on the *unit* of the rates—here, number of people per square mile of land.

Discuss the follow-up question. (You may want to consult the social studies teacher for input on this discussion.) Reasons for the differences in population densities include the following: People tend to cluster along coastal regions. The climate and weather of some regions is more hospitable than that of other regions. Some regions have a large number of cities, which have greater population densities. Some areas are agricultural—the land is used for farming, not for people. Some areas are mountainous and hence inaccessible to large numbers of people.

5.4 • Comparing the Dakotas

In this problem, the idea of "how many for 1" occurs as students explore the question: How many people are there per square mile?

Launch

This problem can flow directly from the summary of Problem 5.3. Have students do part A individually as a quick check of their understanding of population density. Talk about the answer.

Read through part B, which asks how many people would need to move from one state to the other to equalize the population densities in the two states. This is an interesting problem; North and South Dakota have very similar population densities, so we are talking about moving only a small number of people to make the adjustment. This is more difficult than it may appear at first and should be a good challenge for pairs or groups of four.

Explore

Allow groups a few minutes to talk about how to approach the problem, then bring them back together to share their ideas. You may want to write the two ratios on the board or on Transparency 5.4.

$$\text{South Dakota: } \frac{721,000}{75,896} = 9.50 \text{ people per mi}^2$$

$$\text{North Dakota: } \frac{638,000}{68,994} = 9.25 \text{ people per mi}^2$$

> What do we know from these density rates? *(We know that we need to move people from South Dakota to North Dakota, but we don't know how many.)*

Circulate as groups work on the problem, listening to their reasoning. If any groups are having trouble getting started, encourage them to make a reasonable guess and then test their guess.

> Once you get an answer to how many people need to move from South Dakota to North Dakota, how might you test your number to see whether it is correct?

Don't push for an answer; just use this question to get students thinking about how to check their work.

Summarize

Give groups a chance to talk about their estimates and their strategies for solving the problem. Here are two strategies groups have used. The first is a guess-and-test strategy; the second is more sophisticated.

- Belinda's group: "We moved 5000 people to North Dakota to see what it did to the densities. After that move, we had these numbers:

$$\text{South Dakota: } \frac{716,000}{75,896} = 9.43 \text{ people per mi}^2$$

$$\text{North Dakota: } \frac{643,000}{68,994} = 9.32 \text{ people per mi}^2$$

We were moving in the right direction, so we moved 5000 more people.

$$\text{South Dakota: } \frac{711,000}{75,896} = 9.37 \text{ people per mi}^2$$

$$\text{North Dakota: } \frac{648,000}{68,994} = 9.39 \text{ people per mi}^2$$

That was too many, so we tried 9000 in all.

$$\text{South Dakota: } \frac{712,000}{75,896} = 9.38 \text{ people per mi}^2$$

$$\text{North Dakota: } \frac{647,000}{68,994} = 9.38 \text{ people per mi}^2$$

About 9000 people must move from South Dakota to North Dakota."

- Armin's group: "First, we put together all the land area and all the people and computed the overall density.

$$\frac{721,000 + 638,000}{75,896 + 68,994} = \frac{1,359,000}{144,890} = 9.38 \text{ people per mi}^2$$

Then we thought about how to spread out the people so that each state would have this overall density. If we multiply the area of North Dakota by this rate, we get

$$68,994 \times 9.38 = 647,164 \text{ people}$$

This means that about $647,164 - 638,000 = 9164$ people need to move to from South Dakota to North Dakota."

Use the follow-up as a quick check on students' understanding. Direct students to the table on pages 71 and 72 of the student edition, which gives the population of each state. You or the class will need to locate the land area of your state in square miles.

5.5 • Predicting Traffic Jams

This problem is a natural follow-up to Problem 5.4. It applies the idea of density to another context, traffic.

Launch

Ask questions to stimulate a class discussion about the topic.

> In addition to the population of geographical areas, where else is the idea of density important?

Have you ever been in New York City or Mexico City, or seen pictures of the traffic there? How do you think driving in the country is different from driving in a city like New York or Mexico City?

What kinds of comparisons would tell us about the driving conditions in a particular area? Does the idea of density seem reasonable in this context?

Read or explain the data about the three cities. When students understand the context and what they are to do, let groups of two or three tackle the problem.

Explore

Students are asked to compute and compare the ratio of cars and roads as two different rates—cars per unit length of road, and amount of road length per car. You may need to remind students that there are 5280 feet in a mile.

As you circulate, ask questions about the meaning of the rates the groups are finding. Remind students to properly label each quantity they compute.

Summarize

Ask groups to share how they approached the problem. Look for efficient strategies among those reported, and highlight them for the class.

Use the follow-up questions as part of the summary. Many factors other than traffic density may affect the formation of traffic jams. Students may mention such influences as road construction, weather conditions, accidents (along with "rubbernecks"), time of day (rush-hour traffic), and events that draw large numbers of vehicles.

Students may have several ideas for what steps cities like Hong Kong can take to alleviate the problems brought on by too many vehicles crowding too little space. Some cities in the United States restrict some roads and traffic lanes during rush hours to cars with a minimum number of occupants (usually two or three). The HOV (high-occupancy vehicle) lanes encourage car pooling. Mass-transit systems, such as subways and trains, are used by some cities to move people and reduce the number of vehicles on the roads.

Additional Answers

Answers to Problem 5.2

A. Estimates will vary, depending on how many beans are in the container. The basic proportion to be solved in making an estimate of the total number of beans is

$$\frac{\text{number of marked beans in container}}{\text{number of beans in container}} = \frac{\text{number of marked beans in sample}}{\text{number of beans in sample}}$$

Some students use the proportion of total beans to marked beans, or

$$\frac{\text{number of beans in container}}{\text{number of marked beans in container}} = \frac{\text{number of beans in sample}}{\text{number of marked beans in sample}}$$

Some groups may analyze the data for each sample; some may group all the data together before analyzing their results. Here are two groups' answers.

- Andreji's group: "We marked 100 beans and returned them to the jar. Then we took five samples:

Sample	Number of beans	Number of marked beans
1	26	2
2	30	4
3	35	4
4	28	3
5	32	6
Total	**151**	**19**

We set up the ratio $\frac{19}{151} = \frac{100}{?}$. We divided 100 by 19 to find 5.263. Since $\frac{19 \times 5.263}{151 \times 5.263} = \frac{100}{794.7}$, we think we have about 795 beans in our jar."

- Mara's group: "We had a total sample of 172 beans, with 23 marked. We found the ratio of total beans to marked beans as a decimal, $\frac{172}{23} = 7.48$. This means that $7.48 = \frac{?}{100}$, so the ? must be 748 beans in the jar."

B. Biologists might count deer populations using the capture-tag-recapture method by catching a sample of deer, marking them with tags of some sort, and releasing them. Later, the biologists would catch another sample of deer and compute the ratio of tagged deer in the new sample. From this ratio, they would find an equivalent ratio using the total number of tagged deer and the predicted number of deer in the population.

Answers to Problem 5.3

A. Answers will vary.

B–C.

Region	Population density (area per mi²)	Rank
New England	13,270,000 ÷ 62,811 = 211.3	8
Middle Atlantic	38,125,000 ÷ 99,463 = 383.3	9
South Atlantic	46,398,000 ÷ 266,221 = 174.3	6
East North Central	43,184,000 ÷ 243,539 = 177.3	7
East South Central	15,890,000 ÷ 178,615 = 89.0	5
West North Central	18,210,000 ÷ 507,981 = 35.8	2
West South Central	28,404,000 ÷ 426,234 = 66.6	4
Mountain	15,214,000 ÷ 856,121 = 17.8	1
Pacific	41,645,000 ÷ 895,353 = 46.5	3

D. Answers will vary.

Answers to Problem 5.5

C. The city most likely to have a traffic jam is probably the city with the least number of feet per vehicle, as each vehicle will have a smaller amount of road space. Using the other approach—density of vehicles per mile—we would look for the greatest number to identify the city most likely to have a traffic jam. In either case, Hong Kong is the city most likely to have a traffic jam.

ACE Answers

Connections

13a.

Beans in sample	25	50	75	100	150	200	250
Marked beans	3	12	13	17	27	38	52
Percent marked beans	12%	24%	17%	17%	18%	19%	21%

13b.

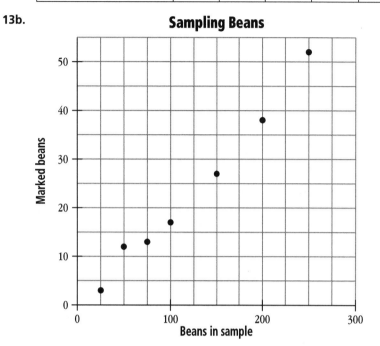

The pattern shows that as the sample size increases, the number of marked beans increases at a fairly steady rate.

13c. The graph will look like this. Note that the graph does not begin at (0, 0) for convenience, and that the connecting line makes the pattern clearer.

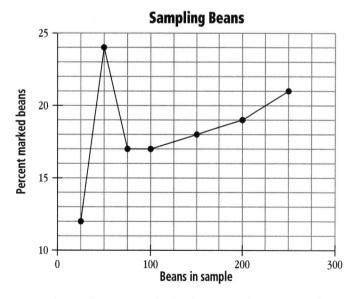

The pattern shows that as sample size increases the percent of marked beans stabilizes. As the sample increases, the percent of marked beans increases fairly steadily. (Note: The stabilizing of proportions in samples, as sample size increases, is identical to the results from probability experiments.)

Mathematical Reflections

1a. You need to find a ratio that is equivalent to the ratio of 3 to 20 in the sample in the form 25 to *what*. Since you have to multiply 3 by 6.67 to get 20, you need to multiply 25 by the same number, which gives $25 \times 6.67 = 166.7$ or about 167 fish.

Or, you can build the sample up like a recipe until you get 25 tagged fish:

Tagged	3	6	9	12	15	18	21	24
Total	20	40	60	80	100	120	140	160

One more tagged fish is $\frac{1}{3}$ of the 3, and since $\frac{1}{3}$ of 20 is 6.67 there are $160 + 6.67 = 166.67$ or about 167 fish.

Choosing Strategies

This investigation engages students in solving a variety of problems using the concepts and strategies they have developed during the unit. In many situations, more than one strategy can be used, so students are given practice in selecting an appropriate strategy.

Problem 6.1, Scaling Up or Down, applies what students learned in the *Stretching and Shrinking* unit about similar figures. Students compare figures using several strategies, including scaling, differences, equivalent ratios, and unit rates. In Problem 6.2, Using Rules of Thumb, students make comparisons using given rules of thumb, or benchmarks, scaling ratios up or down to find the unknown quantities (which is equivalent to solving a proportion). Problem 6.3, Selecting Delegates, is a "fair division" or apportionment problem. Students consider questions about population characteristics that may be relevant in making decisions about who will be invited to an environmental conference to represent their geographic areas.

Mathematical and Problem-Solving Goals

- **To select and apply appropriate strategies to make comparisons**

- **To review when ratio and difference strategies are useful in solving problems**

- **To use proportional reasoning to fairly apportion available space so that the group is representative of the larger community**

Materials

Problem	For students	For the teacher
All	Graphing calculators	Transparencies 6.1 to 6.3 (optional)
6.3	Labsheets 6.3A and 6.3B (optional; 1 of each per group), large sheets of paper (optional; for displaying group work)	Transparencies of Labsheets 6.3A and 6.3B (optional)
ACE	Centimeter and inch grid paper (optional; 1 of each per student)	

Student Pages 65–81   **Teaching the Investigation 81a–81g**

INVESTIGATION 6

Choosing Strategies

So far in this unit, you have used fractions, percents, ratios, rates, and unit rates to make comparisons and to estimate populations and population densities. In this investigation, you will explore several problem situations in which you need to choose a strategy for solving the problem and explain why your strategy makes sense. There will usually be several ways to think about a problem. You will begin to see what kind of reasoning works best for a particular type of problem.

6.1 Scaling Up or Down

Dinosaurs (which means "terrible lizards") roamed the earth for 125 million years. By studying the bones, teeth, and footprints of these ancient reptiles, paleontologists learn more about them. Reconstructing dinosaur skeletons helps these scientists estimate the height, weight, and length of different species of dinosaur.

One of the largest predators of all time was *Tyrannosaurus rex* (which means "king tyrant lizard"). This carnivorous dinosaur lived 70 million years ago in many areas of North America, including the present states of Montana, Wyoming, and Texas. Scientists determined that *T. rex* was a meat eater by studying the shape and size of its head and teeth.

Tips for the Linguistically Diverse Classroom

Visual Enhancement The Visual Enhancement technique is described in detail in *Getting to Know Connected Mathematics*. It involves using real objects or pictures to make information more comprehensible. Example: While discussing Problem 6.1, you might show pictures of dinosaurs and point out the varying shapes and sizes of heads, teeth, bones, and footprints.

6.1

Scaling Up or Down

At a Glance

Grouping: pairs or small groups

Launch

- Review the information about dinosaurs, including the data about *T. rex* and humans.

Explore

- Have pairs or groups explore the problem (with each student writing his or her own paragraph) and answer the follow-up questions.

Summarize

- Let each group offer an interesting comparison and explain how they made it.

- Briefly review the follow-up questions.

- Ask more questions that apply the ideas of similarity to the adolescent and adult *T. rex*. *(optional)*

Assignment Choices

ACE questions 1, 10, 11, 14 (you may want to distribute Labsheet 6.ACE), and unassigned choices from earlier problems

Problem 6.1

T. rex weighed about 8,100 kilograms and reached heights of up to 6 meters—almost as tall as a two-story house! Archeologists have uncovered *T. rex* skulls 1 meter long and *T. rex* incisors (the longest teeth) 15 centimeters long.

A "larger than average" human being can be about 2 meters tall and weigh 90 kilograms. Human incisors are about 1 centimeter long, and a large human skull can be about 20 centimeters long.

How big was *T. rex* compared to a "larger than average" human being?

Write a paragraph to help someone younger than you understand how the size of *T. rex* compares to the size of a human. Be very specific about the comparisons you are making.

■ Problem 6.1 Follow-Up

1. Suppose an infant *T. rex* was the same height as the human described in the problem and was similar to an adult *T. rex*. What would be the scale factor between a grown *T. rex* and the infant *T. rex*?

2. How long were the incisors of this young *T. rex*?

3. How long was the skull of this young *T. rex*?

Answer to Problem 6.1

See page 81d.

Answers to Problem 6.1 Follow-Up

1. The scale factor would be 6 ÷ 2 = 3.

2. 15 cm ÷ 3 = 5 cm long

3. 1 m ÷ 3 = $\frac{1}{3}$ m or $33\frac{1}{3}$ cm long

6.2 Using Rules of Thumb

Carpenters, bakers, tailors, designers, and people in many other occupations use rules of thumb to make quick estimates. A *rule of thumb* is a method of estimating, based on experience and common sense, that is practical but not necessarily precise. For example, you may have heard someone say, "A pint is a pound the world around." This rule of thumb tells how to compare liquid measures with weight. Since 1 quart is equal to 2 pints, you can use this rule of thumb to estimate that 1 quart of milk weighs about 2 pounds. In this problem, you will be working with several rules of thumb.

Problem 6.2

In A–D, use the given rule of thumb to solve the problem. Explain how you found each answer.

A. *It takes about 100 maple trees to make 25 gallons of maple syrup.*
Mr. Paulo made maple syrup from all of his sugar maple trees. He ended up with 16 gallons of syrup. About how many sugar maple trees does he have?

B. *A 5-minute shower requires about 18 gallons of water.*
About how much water do you use for an 8-minute shower? How much water will you use if you take an 8-minute shower every day for a year?

C. *A double-spaced page of text contains about 250 words if it is printed in Times with a font size of 12, and about 330 words if it is printed in Times with a font size of 10.*
Jeremy printed his term paper in the computer lab. He used 10-point Times, and the paper came to 15 double-spaced pages. Jeremy's teacher requires term papers be 20 double-spaced pages long. If Jeremy changes the font to 12-point Times, how long will his paper be?

D. *Jogging burns about 100 calories per mile.*
Elizabeth jogs at a rate of 4.5 miles per hour. How long will it take her to burn off the 1200-calorie lunch she ate at Burger Heaven?

Adapted from *Rules of Thumb* by Tom Parker. Boston: Houghton Mifflin, 1993.

▓ Problem 6.2 Follow-Up

Ask adults you know if they use any rules of thumb in their jobs or at home. Write down one of the rules you learn. Write a problem that can be solved using the rule.

▪▪▪ At a Glance

Grouping: pairs or small groups

Launch

- Talk with the class about rules of thumb and how they are used.

- Review each rule of thumb in the problem, making sure students understand them.

Explore

- Have individuals think about each rule of thumb. *(optional)*

- Have pairs or groups discuss the rules of thumb and strategies for solving the problems.

- Remind students to label their quantities carefully.

Summarize

- Have groups share and compare their strategies for solving the problems.

- Assign the follow-up as homework.

Answers to Problem 6.2

A. Possible answers: Since it takes 100 ÷ 25 = 4 trees for 1 gallon, 16 gallons will take 4 × 16 = 64 trees. *Using equal ratios:* $\frac{100}{25} = \frac{x}{16}$, so $x = 64$. Some students may make and reason from a rate table.

B. See page 81d.

C. The number of words in the 15 pages is 15 pages × 330 words per page = 4950 words. In 12-point Times, the paper will be 4950 words ÷ 250 words per page = 19.8 pages or about 20 pages long, so Jeremy's teacher will accept it.

D. See page 81d.

Answer to Problem 6.2 Follow-Up

Answers will vary.

Assignment Choices

ACE questions 2, 3, 5–8, and unassigned choices from earlier problems

Selecting Delegates

Grouping: individuals, pairs, or groups

Launch

- Talk about the "Think about this!" feature. *(optional)*

- As a class, review the proportion example on page 69. *(optional)*

Explore

- Have groups explore the problem in class, or assign it as a project.

- Distribute Labsheets 6.3A and 6.3B and large sheets of paper. *(optional)*

- Offer help to groups having trouble reading the table.

Summarize

- Allow groups to share something interesting they discovered.

- Have students further research the demographics of their own region.

Assignment Choices

ACE questions 4, 9, 12, 13, and unassigned choices from earlier problems

---

Young people all over the world are concerned about protecting and improving the environment. American Students for the Environment is hosting a two-week environmental studies conference for 1000 middle-school students from all over the United States. Delegates for the conference will be selected to represent the diversity of the United States population—geographically, ethnically, and economically. Imagine that you are a member of the delegate selection committee.

American Students for the Environment
present

The First Annual

ENVIRONMENTALSTUDIES CONFERENCE

Welcome Delegates!

Think about this!

To make fair decisions about the delegates, you must consider several questions. Tell what information you would need to make each decision below.

- How many of the 1000 delegates should come from each of the nine census regions of the United States?

- What percent of the delegates should represent metropolitan areas, and what percent should represent rural areas?

- What percent of the delegates should represent minority groups?

You and the rest of the delegate selection committe will be using data from the 1990 United States Census to help you make your selections. To choose the number of delegates from each region, you can compare the population of each region to the population of the United States. This ratio can be written as a fraction.

$$\frac{\text{population of the region}}{\text{population of the U.S.}}$$

To give each region a fair number of delegates, it makes sense to make the ratio of delegates equivalent to the ratio of populations. This can be written as an equation:

$$\frac{\text{population of the region}}{\text{population of the U.S.}} = \frac{\text{delegates from the region}}{\text{total number of delegates}}$$

A statement about equivalent ratios or fractions, such as the one above, is called a **proportion.**

To figure out how many delegates should be chosen from a given region, you need to solve the corresponding proportion. For example, the 1990 population of the South Atlantic region of the United States was about 45 million people, and the total population of the United States was about 250 million people. To find the number of conference delegates who should come from the South Atlantic region, you need to solve the proportion

$$\frac{45,000,000}{250,000,000} = \frac{\text{delegates from South Atlantic region}}{1000}$$

Using what you know about equivalent fractions, you could write

$$\frac{45,000,000}{250,000,000} = \frac{45}{250}$$
$$= \frac{180}{1000}$$

and conclude that the South Atlantic region should have 180 delegates.

Problem 6.3

The table on pages 71 and 72 gives data about the United States population. Use the table to help you answer these questions.

A. How many of the 1000 delegates should be chosen from each of the nine geographic regions?

B. How many of the 1000 delegates should be from metropolitan areas, and how many should be from rural areas?

C. How many of the delegates should be of Hispanic origin?

D. Four racial groups are named in the data: white; black; Native American–Eskimo–Aleut; and Asian–Pacific Islander. How many of the total 1000 delegates should represent each of these races? How many should represent the category "all other races" (which is not mentioned in the data)?

E. Use your answers to A–D to help you develop a plan for selecting the delegates. Describe your plan in a report that you could submit to the conference organizers.

■ **Problem 6.3 Follow-Up**

If you could add another criterion to help choose the delegates so that the representation would be fair, what criterion would you add and why?

Answers to Problem 6.3

See page 81e.

Answer to Problem 6.3 Follow-Up

Other criteria students might mention include gender, age, and family income.

U.S. 1990 Population by Region, Race, and Metro/Rural Location
(All Numbers in 1000s)

	Total	Metro areas	Rural areas	White	Black	Hispanic*	Native American, Eskimo, Aleut	Asian, Pacific Islander
United States	248,710	192,726	55,984	199,686	29,986	22,354	1959	7274
New England	13,207	10,598	2609	12,033	628	568	33	232
Maine	1228	441	787	1208	5	7	6	7
New Hampshire	1109	622	487	1087	7	11	2	9
Vermont	563	131	431	555	2	4	2	3
Massachusetts	6016	5438	578	5405	300	288	12	143
Rhode Island	1003	928	75	917	39	46	4	18
Connecticut	3287	3038	250	2859	274	213	7	51
Middle Atlantic	37,602	34,193	3409	30,036	4986	3186	92	1104
New York	17,990	16,386	1605	13,385	2859	2214	63	694
New Jersey	7730	7730	n/a	6130	1037	740	15	273
Pennsylvania	11,882	10,077	1805	10,520	1090	232	15	137
East North Central	42,009	32,557	9452	35,764	4817	1438	150	573
Ohio	10,847	8567	2280	9522	1155	140	20	91
Indiana	5544	3796	1748	5021	432	99	13	38
Illinois	11,431	9450	1981	8953	1694	904	22	285
Michigan	9295	7446	1850	7756	1292	202	56	105
Wisconsin	4892	3298	1593	4513	245	93	39	54
West North Central	17,660	10,132	7528	16,254	899	289	188	195
Minnesota	4375	2960	1415	4130	95	54	50	78
Iowa	2777	1223	1554	2683	48	33	7	25
Missouri	5117	3387	1730	4486	548	62	20	41
North Dakota	639	257	381	604	4	5	26	3
South Dakota	696	205	491	638	3	5	51	3
Nebraska	1578	766	812	1481	57	37	12	12
Kansas	2478	1333	1145	2232	143	94	22	32
South Atlantic	43,567	32,461	11,106	33,391	8924	2133	172	631
Delaware	666	442	224	535	112	16	2	9
Maryland	4781	4439	343	3394	1190	125	13	140
District of Columbia	607	607	n/a	180	400	33	1	11
Virginia	6187	4483	1704	4792	1163	160	15	159
West Virginia	1793	653	1140	1726	56	8	2	7
North Carolina	6629	3758	2871	5008	1456	77	80	52
South Carolina	3487	2113	1374	2407	1040	31	8	22
Georgia	6478	4212	2266	4600	1747	109	13	76
Florida	12,938	11,754	1184	10,749	1760	1574	36	154
East South Central	15,176	8513	6663	12,049	2977	95	41	84
Kentucky	3685	1714	1971	3392	263	22	6	18
Tennessee	4877	3300	1577	4048	778	33	10	32
Alabama	4041	2723	1317	2976	1021	25	17	22
Mississippi	2576	776	1798	1633	915	16	9	13

	Total	Metro areas	Rural areas	White	Black	Hispanic*	Native American, Eskimo, Aleut	Asian, Pacific Islander
West South Central	**26,703**	**19,614**	**7,089**	**20,142**	**3929**	**4539**	**350**	**407**
Arkansas	2351	943	1408	1945	374	20	13	13
Louisiana	4220	2935	1285	2839	1299	93	19	41
Oklahoma	3146	1870	1276	2584	234	86	252	34
Texas	16,987	13,867	3119	12,775	2022	4340	66	319
Mountain	**13,659**	**9179**	**4480**	**11,762**	**374**	**1992**	**481**	**217**
Montana	799	191	608	741	2	12	48	4
Idaho	1007	206	801	950	3	53	14	9
Wyoming	454	134	319	427	4	26	9	3
Colorado	3294	2686	608	2905	133	424	28	60
New Mexico	1515	733	782	1146	30	579	134	14
Arizona	3665	2896	769	2963	111	688	204	55
Utah	1723	1336	387	1616	12	85	24	33
Nevada	1202	996	206	1013	79	124	20	38
Pacific	**39,127**	**35,479**	**3648**	**28,255**	**2454**	**8114**	**453**	**3831**
Washington	4867	3976	891	4309	150	215	81	211
Oregon	2842	1947	895	2637	46	113	38	69
California	29,760	28,493	1267	20,524	2209	7688	242	2846
Alaska	550	226	324	415	22	18	86	20
Hawaii	1108	836	272	370	27	81	5	685

*Persons of Hispanic origin may be of any race.

Totals include other races, which are not shown separately. N/A means not applicable.

Source: *Statistical Abstract of the United States 1993.* Published by the Bureau of the Census, Washington, D.C., p. 254.

As you work on these ACE questions, use your calculator whenever you need it.

Applications

1. In a free-throw contest at the environmental studies conference, Clifford, a delegate from New England, made 10 out of 15 shots. Suppose Clifford's success rate stays the same for his next 100 shots. Write and solve proportions to answer these questions.

   a. How many shots will Clifford make out of his next 60 shots?

   b. How many shots will Clifford make out of his next 80 shots?

   c. How many shots will it take for Clifford to make 30 more free-throws?

   d. How many shots will it take for him to make 45 more free-throws?

2. The conference organizers ordered environmental buttons for the participants to wear. They paid $18 for 12 dozen buttons. Write and solve proportions to answer these questions.

   a. How much do 4 dozen buttons cost?

   b. How much do 50 dozen buttons cost?

   c. How many dozens of buttons can the organizers buy for $27?

   d. How many dozens of buttons can the organizers buy for $63?

3. Middletown decided to sponsor a two-day meeting for its own middle-school students to study local environmental problems. There are three middle schools in Middletown: Red Middle School with 618 students, White Middle School with 378 students, and Blue Middle School with 204 students. If 20 student delegates in all will attend the conference, how many should be selected from each school?

Answers

Applications

1a. Clifford's rate of success is $\frac{10}{15}$ or $\frac{2}{3}$. Since $\frac{2}{3} = \frac{\text{shots made}}{60} = \frac{40}{60}$, Clifford would make 40 shots.

1b. Since $\frac{2}{3} = \frac{\text{shots made}}{80} = $ about $\frac{53}{80}$, Clifford will make about 53 shots.

1c. Since $\frac{2}{3} = \frac{30}{\text{shots taken}} = \frac{30}{45}$, it will take Clifford 45 shots to make 30 free-throws.

1d. Since $\frac{2}{3} = \frac{45}{\text{shots taken}} = $ about $\frac{45}{68}$, it will take Clifford about 68 shots to make 45 free-throws.

2a. The buttons are $\frac{12\,\text{dozen}}{18\,\text{dollars}}$ or $\frac{2\,\text{dozen}}{3\,\text{dollars}}$. Since $\frac{2}{3} = \frac{4}{\text{cost for 4 dozen}} = \frac{4}{6}$, 4 dozen buttons would cost $6.

2b–d. See below left.

3. See below left.

2b. Since $\frac{2}{3} = \frac{50}{\text{cost for 50 dozen}} = \frac{50}{75}$, 50 dozen buttons would cost $75.

2c. Since $\frac{2}{3} = \frac{\text{dozens of buttons}}{27} = \frac{18}{27}$, the organizers can buy 18 dozen buttons.

2d. Since $\frac{2}{3} = \frac{\text{dozens of buttons}}{63} = \frac{42}{63}$, the organizers can buy 42 dozen buttons.

3. Altogether, the schools have 618 + 378 + 204 = 1200 students.

School	Ratio	Delegates
Red	$\frac{618}{1200} = \frac{\text{no. of delegates}}{20} = \frac{10.3}{20}$	10
White	$\frac{378}{1200} = \frac{\text{no. of delegates}}{20} = \frac{6.3}{20}$	6
Blue	$\frac{204}{1200} = \frac{\text{no. of delegates}}{20} = \frac{3.4}{20}$	3

Students will have to adjust their distribution if their total is under or over 20. There is no standard rule for resolving such apportionment questions.

4a. See page 81f.

4b. Answers will vary. The new distribution affects various regions substantially.

4c. Possible answer: Using land area is a reasonable means of determining delegates because so many environmental issues deal with keeping soil and water from becoming polluted. Using population is fair because areas should have a voice equal to their population.

5a. $26 \times \frac{1}{4} = 6.5$ mi

5b. $5 \times 4 = 20$ mi

4. This table gives the total land area of each census region in the United States.

Census region	Area (square miles)
New England	62,811
Middle Atlantic	99,463
East North Central	266,221
West North Central	243,539
South Atlantic	178,615
East South Central	507,981
West South Central	426,234
Mountain	856,121
Pacific	895,353

a. Suppose the delegates for the environmental conference in Problem 6.3 were selected using the ratio of the area of the census region to the area of the United States. Use the data above to figure out how many delegates should attend from each region.

b. In part a, you determined the number of delegates from each region by comparing land areas. In part A of Problem 6.3, you determined the number of delegates from each region by comparing populations. For each region, discuss how these numbers compare.

c. Give one reason why each system of choosing delegates (using land areas or using populations) might be fair.

5. Swimming a quarter of a mile burns about the same number of calories as running a mile.

a. Gilda runs a 26-mile marathon. How far would her sister have to swim to burn the same number of calories Gilda burned during the marathon?

b. Jack swims 5 miles a day. How many miles would he have to run to burn the same number of calories he burns during his daily swim?

Connections

6. Which is the better buy: a 14-ounce box of Cruncho cereal for $1.98, or a 36-ounce box of Cruncho cereal for $2.59?

7. Which is the better average: 10 free-throws out of 15, or 8 free-throws out of 10?

8. Which is the better home-run rate: hitting 2 home runs in 6 times at bat, or hitting 5 home runs in 12 times at bat?

9. The population of the United States in 1994 was about 260,651,000. The land area of the United States is 3,536,338 square miles. If the people in the United States were spread uniformly throughout the states, how many people would there be per square mile? Compare your answer with the population density of your state.

10. The picture below is drawn on a centimeter grid.

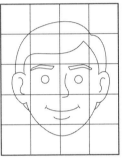

   a. On a grid made of larger squares than those shown here, draw a figure similar to this figure. What is the scale factor between the original figure and your drawing?

   b. Draw another figure similar to this one, but use a grid made of smaller squares than those shown here. What is the scale factor between the original and your drawing?

11. Anna is making a circular spinner to be used at the school carnival. She wants the spinner to be divided so that 30% of the area is blue, 20% is red, 15% is green, and 35% is yellow. Design a spinner that meets her specifications.

Connections

(Note: In 6–10, students may use various ways to compare the rates. It is important that they understand that different comparisons may be valid. You may want to discuss some of the methods they use.)

6. The 14-oz box is $\frac{1.98}{14}$ = 14¢ per oz, and the 36-oz box is $\frac{2.59}{36}$ = 7¢ per oz. The 36-oz box is the better buy.

7. Since $\frac{10}{15} = \frac{20}{30}$ and $\frac{8}{10} = \frac{24}{30}$, 8 out of 10 is the better average.

8. Since $\frac{2}{6} = \frac{4}{12}$, 5 home runs in 12 times at bat is the better rate.

9. $\frac{260,651,000}{3,536,338}$ is about 74 people per mi².

10a. Answers will depend on the size of the new grid. If the new grid has 2-centimeter squares, the scale factor from the original to the enlargement is 2.

10b. Answers will vary. The scale factor from the original to the new drawing will be less than 1.

11. See below left.

11. Possible answer:

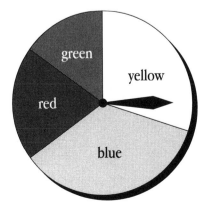

(Note: Students may want to use an angle ruler to divide a circle into the given percentages.)

Extensions

12. Below is a table of data from a middle school class showing each student's household's water use for one week and the number of people in the household.

Our Water Use

Student (initials)	People in household	Water use (gallons)	Rate of water use (gallons/person)
RE	5	1901	
TW	4	1682	
HW	5	1493	
WE	4	1336	
GK	5	1332	
DJ	6	1309	
MJ	5	1231	
WD	5	1231	
MA	5	1204	
LR	5	1031	
FP	4	986	
HA	5	985	
TB	3	940	
CH	5	938	
ME	4	924	
JW	4	910	
PR	4	843	
NP	3	819	
BH	4	807	
EB	4	755	
PJ	4	726	
HJ	4	641	
HM	3	554	
JZ	2	493	

a. Calculate the rate of water use per person in each household.

b. Combine all the data to find the rate of water use overall.

c. Round your answers in part a to the nearest 10. Make a stem plot showing the rate of water use per person in each household. Start your stem plot like this:

```
4 | 2
3 | 8  0
2 |                Key
1 |                4 | 2 means 420
```

d. The two *histograms* below and on the next page display the information about gallons of water used per person in each household. Compare the two histograms and explain how they differ.

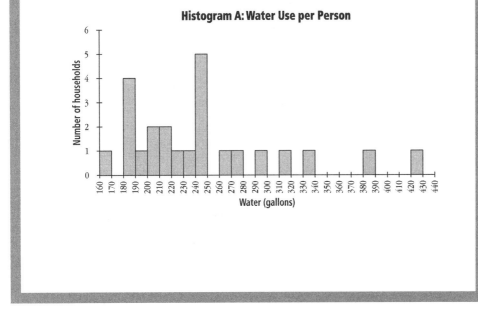

Histogram A: Water Use per Person

Extensions

12a, b. See page 81f.

12c. See below left.

12d. Histogram A shows water use in 10-gallon increments. Histogram B shows water use in 25-gallon increments.

12c. The second stem plot shows the numbers in each leaf ordered.

```
4 | 2                          4 | 2
3 | 8 0 3 1                    3 | 0 1 3 8
2 | 7 2 5 5 4 1 5 0 3 3 1 7 0 5    2 | 0 0 1 1 2 3 3 4 5 5 5 5 7 7
1 | 9 9 8 6 8                  1 | 6 8 8 9 9
```

12e. The stem plot does not look like either histogram. The water-use rates in the stem plot are shown in groups of 100 gallons. Histograms A and B show water use in groups of 10 and 25 gallons, respectively.

12f. If a person with a 270 gal/person rate was added, the bar in Histogram A that corresponds to the interval 270–280 would be one unit higher. In Histogram B, the bar that corresponds to the interval 260–285 would be one unit higher.

12g. The typical amount of water used per person per week can be described in several ways. From the table, the mean is 245.8 gal/person. From the ordered stem plot, the median is in the interval 230–240 gal/person. From Histogram A, the median is in the interval 230–250 gal/person, and from Histogram B, the median is in the interval 210–260 gal/person.

12h. See page 81g.

13a. The number of representatives from each state is determined by the ratio of the population of the state to the population of the United States.

13b. Each state is allowed two senators.

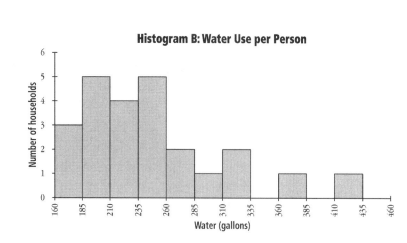

Histogram B: Water Use per Person

e. Does your stem plot from part c look like either histogram?

f. Suppose a new student joined the class and her household used 270 gallons of water per person. How would this student's data be indicated on Histogram A and Histogram B?

g. What is the typical number of gallons of water used per person in one week? Justify your answer, using Histograms A and B and your stem plot to help you explain.

h. Make Histogram C by grouping the data in intervals of 30 gallons. Now which graph—A, B, or C—would be the most useful to help you answer the question in part g? Why?

13. The people of the United States are represented in Congress in two ways: each state has representatives in the House of Representatives, and each state has senators in the Senate.

a. The number of representatives from each state in the House of Representatives varies from state to state. How is the number of representatives from each state determined?

b. How is the number of senators from each state determined?

c. Compare the two methods of determining representation in Congress. What are the advantages and disadvantages of these two forms of representation?

A meeting of the House of Representatives

14. The very small country of Trig has three states: Sine, Cosine, and Tangent, with populations of 59, 76, and 14, respectively. The Trig Congress has 35 members.

a. Using a method that you think is fair to all states, determine the number of representatives from each state. Explain your reasoning.

b. How would the number of representatives from each state change if there were 37 members of Congress?

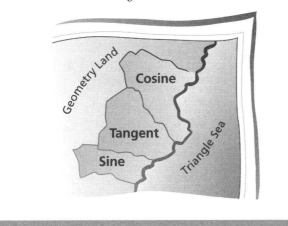

13c. Answers will vary. In the Senate, states with a small population, like Vermont, will have an equal voice against a state with a large population. In the House of Representatives, states with more people have more representatives and thus more influence.

14a. See below left.

14b. Since $\frac{149}{37} = 4.03$, the number of representatives would now be 15, 19, and 3, respectively. Or, $\frac{59}{149} \times 37 = 14.65 =$ about 15; $\frac{76}{149} \times 37 = 18.87 =$ about 19; and $\frac{14}{149} \times 37 = 3.48 =$ about 3.

14a. Since $\frac{59 + 76 + 14}{35} = \frac{149}{35} = 4.26$, there could be one representative for every 4.26 people—14, 18, and 3, respectively. Or, since the population of Trig is 149:

State	Population	Ratio	Representatives
Sine	59	$\frac{59}{149} = \frac{\text{no. of reps.}}{35} = \frac{13.9}{35}$	14
Cosine	76	$\frac{76}{149} = \frac{\text{no. of reps.}}{35} = \frac{17.9}{35}$	18
Tangent	14	$\frac{14}{149} = \frac{\text{no. of reps.}}{35} = \frac{3.3}{35}$	3

15a. The total amount of water used by Ryan's family was $1 \times 17.3 + 3 \times 13.4 + 2 \times 9.5 = 76.5$ gal.

15b. In a year, his family will use $52 \times 76.5 = 3978$ gal.

15. Ryan asked his family to mark on a chart whenever they washed a load of laundry. Here is his family's chart for one week:

	Sun.	Mon.	Tues.	Wed.	Thurs.	Fri.	Sat.
Large load					X		
Medium load		X		X	X		
Small load			X		X		

a. Using the following information about rate of water use, estimate the total amount of water Ryan's family used for washing laundry during the week. Explain your answer.

Large-capacity washing machines use approximately
- 9.5 gallons of water for a small load
- 13.4 gallons of water for a medium load
- 17.3 gallons of water for a large load

b. If this is a typical week, how much water does Ryan's family use in one year for washing laundry?

Mathematical Reflections

In this investigation, you used ratios, rates, percents, fractions, and proportions to solve problems. You thought about which methods of making comparisons would be helpful in solving particular types of problems. These questions will help you summarize what you have learned:

1 a. Describe a situation in which finding a rate is a good strategy for making comparisons. Tell why you think your situation calls for finding a rate.

b. Describe a situation in which finding a unit rate is a good strategy for making comparisons. Tell why you think your situation calls for finding a unit rate.

2 There are 17 girls and 13 boys in Mr. Baldridge's class. Write every comparison you can think of that can be formed from this information. Describe what each comparison shows.

3 Rodrigo drove his car 400 miles and used 12 gallons of gas. Write two rates that tell about this situation, and explain what each shows.

4 If you know that 4 cans of chili feed 6 people, how many cans of chili will feed 240 people? How many people can you feed with 45 cans of chili? Explain your answers.

5 How do you recognize a situation in which you need to use a ratio comparison rather than simply finding differences?

Think about your answers to these questions, discuss your ideas with other students and your teacher, and then write a summary of your findings in your journal.

Tips for the Linguistically Diverse Classroom

Diagram Code The Diagram Code technique is described in detail in *Getting to Know Connected Mathematics*. Students use a minimal number of words and drawings, diagrams, or symbols to respond to questions that require writing. Example: Question 2—A student might answer this question by drawing a group of boys and labeling the drawing *43%*; drawing stick figures of 17 girls and 13 boys and labeling the drawing *17 girls to 13 boys*; and drawing stick figures of 4 girls labeled *4 more* (girl stick figure) *than* (boy stick figure).

Possible Answers

1a. Finding a rate is a good strategy for comparing the number of boys and girls in two classes. For example, Ms. Beyers' homeroom has 20 boys and 12 girls (a rate of 5 boys to 3 girls), and Mr. Apple's homeroom has 18 boys and 12 girls (a rate of 6 boys to 3 girls). Or, if we know that 5 computer disks cost $4 and we want to know how much 45 disks would cost, we can scale 5:4 up to 45:36; they would cost $36.

1b. Finding a unit rate is a good strategy when you want to evaluate which offer is a better buy; for example, 16 candy bars for $12 or 5 candy bars for $4. The unit rates will tell us how much per bar in each case (75¢ and 80¢). Unit rates can help consumers make informed choices.

2. Some possible comparisons are 17 girls to 13 boys; 17 girls to 30 students; 1 boy per about 1.3 girls; approximately 43% of the class are boys; there are 4 more girls than boys. (Students should explain what each comparison shows.)

3. The rate 400 miles to 12 gallons of gas shows the relationship between gallons and miles. The rate 33.3 miles per gallon of gas (or the rate 0.03 gallons per mile) is a unit rate that can be used to calculate the amount of gas needed for a trip.

4. See page 82.

5. See page 82.

TEACHING THE INVESTIGATION

6.1 • Scaling Up or Down

Many students find the topic of dinosaurs fascinating. Review the information in the student edition about dinosaurs and *Tyrannosaurus rex* in particular.

Launch

Launch the investigation by going over the relevant data about *T. rex* and humans.

Explore

Have the class explore this problem in pairs or groups, but each student should write his or her own paragraph. You may want to have each pair or group write their paragraphs on an oversized sheet of paper, illustrating them if they would like to, and display them on a bulletin board. Assign the follow-up questions to be done in the groups after students have competed the problem and posted their group solutions.

The skull length given for *T. rex* is in meters, while that given for humans is in centimeters. If you see groups ignoring this difference, help them to realize that they must express the quantities in the same units in order to compare them.

Summarize

One at a time, have groups say something interesting about their comparisons and how they found them. This can be repeated until no new information is presented. *T. rex* and the human being are not necessarily similar, but students can make comparisons between the dinosaur and the human by using ratios or differences. Some of the comparisons that students might make are discussed in the answers to this problem.

Briefly discuss the follow-up questions. The follow-up assumes that the adult *T. rex* is similar to the adolescent *T. rex*. Be sure to make the connection to similar figures. If two figures are similar, the ratio of corresponding side lengths are equivalent. Since the heights are 6 meters to 2 meters, the scale factor between them is 3.

You could give students the hypothetical area or length of a body part of the adolescent *T. rex* and ask for the related area or length of the adult's body part. In similar figures, the area grows by the square of the scale factor.

> Suppose the area of the baby's footprint is 450 square centimeters. What is the area of the adult *T. rex*'s footprint? *(450 × 9 = 4050 cm²)*

6.2 • Using Rules of Thumb

In this problem, students make comparisons using given benchmarks, scaling ratios to find unknown quantities.

Launch

Ask the class whether they know any rules of thumb; they may have some interesting examples. Some may use rules of thumb in sports. Offer the rule of thumb, "A yard is the distance from my nose to my fingertip when my arm is outstretched." Ask what it means and how it might be helpful. (This rule of thumb is often used by seamstresses to measure material.) Make the connection to benchmarks: rules of thumb like this one allow us to estimate common quantities quickly.

Display or read each rule of thumb in the problem, and verify that the class understands what each is saying.

Explore

Let the class work in pairs (or groups, if you are confident that each student is actively engaged in the thinking process). Or, have students individually think about the rules, then move them into pairs or groups to discuss their strategies.

Students may need to be reminded to be careful about the units and to label each quantity they record. Remind them to write the units for each step of their solutions.

Look for the different ways students are thinking about each problem, and make sure those strategies are shared in the summary.

Summarize

Ask someone from each group to talk about the group's strategy for one of the problems. Following each presentation, allow other groups to share how they did the problem. (If you don't have enough time for this, wait until the solutions to all of problems have been given, then reflect on the various strategies.) Some students may comment that they prefer the way another group thought about the problem. If so, ask why—was the other solution shorter? more efficient? more general?

Assign the follow-up as a homework problem.

▰▰ 6.3 • Selecting Delegates

This problem gives students a chance to explore an open-ended problem, one with several conditions. If the organizers of an environmental conference want the delegates as representative of the diversity of the United States as possible, how many students from each region should be invited? Students use data from the 1990 United States census to make their decisions. The problem will also help to develop students' number sense about large numbers.

Launch

You may choose to orient students to the problem by having an open discussion of the "Think about this!" questions on page 68 of the student edition. Display the U.S. census regions shown on Transparency 6.3A, or refer students to the map shown on page 55.

What would you need to know to answer the questions in the "Think about this"?

What guesses or estimates do you have for the kind of data you would find in the United States census that relates to these questions?

Encourage a variety of proposals, as long as students can give some rationale for their ideas. Some students might argue that the 1000 delegates should be evenly divided among the nine regions. (This is similar to how Senators are chosen for the United States Congress. However, the problem is asking for a division based on population, similar to how United States representatives are chosen.)

This discussion should lead to a consideration of the ratio or fraction of the total population in each representation region. It should be natural to focus on proportions like that set up on page 69 of the student edition. You may want to work through that example as a class before setting students to work on the problem. Ask the class to make sense of the ratio of the populations, $\frac{45,000,000}{250,000,000}$. They should recognize that this is equivalent to $\frac{45}{250}$ or about $\frac{1}{5}$. If they do not see this, discuss why they are equivalent. They should also note that the populations in this ratio have been rounded; your class may want to round the numbers before they start.

Explore

This investigation can be done in class by groups or can be assigned as a project for individuals, pairs, or larger groups. You may want to distribute Labsheets 6.3A and 6.3B, which contain the table of data. Different members of the group could work on different aspects of the problem. If you want groups to prepare their work for a bulletin board display, give each group a large sheet of paper.

Look for groups who are having trouble reading the census data, and offer help where needed. While one goal of the problem is for students to deal with the kinds of data tables typically given in publications, the main goal is for them to develop and apply their mathematical reasoning.

Among other strategies, students might propose finding the number of delegates from each region and then by racial group or by metropolitan or rural area within the regions. In fact, an alternate way to pose parts B, C, and D is to ask the class to use the number of delegates assigned to their region and then determine how many of these would be from each group.

After groups have had some time to work on the problem, you may want to have groups compare their plans to consider whether they are feasible before they do lots of calculations.

Summarize

Ask each group to say something interesting about the problem and the strategies they used. Make sure students understand the strategies that are shared so that all students have some means of addressing the problem.

Students may be particularly interested in the demographics of their own region. Allow them time to explore these and to make comparisons with other regions. This would make an interesting project to do with the social science class.

Additional Answers

Answer to Problem 6.1

Offered here are some comparisons students might make.

Height: *T. rex* is 3 times as tall as the human; the human is $\frac{1}{3}$ as tall as *T. rex*. If three humans stood on top of each other, their total height would be equal to *T. rex*'s height. *(This uses scaling.)* The ratio of heights is 6 to 2, or 3 to 1, or $\frac{3}{1}$ from *T. rex* to the human. *(This uses ratios or rates.)* The difference in heights is 4 m. *(This uses differences. If this answer arises, ask students whether this helps make sense of the relative heights of* T. rex *and the human.)*

Length of skull: *T. rex*'s skull is 5 times the length of the human's skull; the human skull is $\frac{1}{5}$ as long as *T. rex*'s skull. *(This uses scaling.)* The ratio of the skulls is 1 m to 20 cm, or 100 cm to 20 cm, or 5 cm to 1 cm, or $\frac{5}{1}$. *(This uses ratios or rates.)* *T. rex*'s skull is 80 cm longer than the human's skull. *(This uses differences.)*

Incisors: *T. rex*'s incisor is 15 times the length of the human's incisor; the human's incisor is $\frac{1}{15}$ the length of *T. rex*'s incisor. *(This uses scaling.)* The ratio of the length of *T. rex*'s incisor to that of the human's incisor is 15 to 1. *(This uses rates.)* *T. rex*'s incisor is 14 cm longer than the human's incisor. *(This uses differences.)*

Weight: *T. rex*'s weight is 90 times greater than a human's weight; the weight of the human is $\frac{1}{90}$ that of *T. rex*. *(This uses scaling.)* The ratio of the weights is 8,100 to 90, or 90 to 1. *(This uses ratios or rates.)* *T. rex* weighs 8010 kilograms more than the human. *(This uses differences.)*

For the Teacher: Different Ratios

You might point out that the ratio of weights, $\frac{8100}{90} = \frac{90}{1}$, does not look like the ratio of heights, $\frac{6}{2} = \frac{3}{1}$. In other words, weight does not scale with height. You might also show that the ratio of incisor lengths ($\frac{15}{1}$) and skull lengths ($\frac{100}{20} = \frac{5}{1}$) are not the same as the ratio of heights.

Answers to Problem 6.2

B. Possible answers: *Using unit rates:* Since $\frac{18 \text{ gal}}{5 \text{ min}}$ = 3.6 gal/min, an 8-minute shower takes 8 × 3.6 = 28.8 gal, and for 365 days would require 28.8 × 365 = 10,512 gal. *Using equal ratios:* $\frac{18}{5} = \frac{x}{8}$ (or $\frac{18 \times 8}{5 \times 8} = \frac{5 \times x}{5 \times 8}$), so x = 18 × $\frac{8}{5}$ = 28.8 gal for an 8-minute shower, or 28.8 × 365 = 10,512 gal over a year. (If students choose this strategy, they may need help or redirection.) *Using another version of this proportion approach:* Students could reason that $\frac{18 \text{ gal}}{5 \text{ min}} \rightarrow \frac{?}{1 \text{ min}} \rightarrow \frac{?}{8 \text{ min}}$ and solve for the unknown quantities.

D. Possible answers: *Using a rate table:* We can see that Elizabeth must run 12 miles:

Calories burned	100	200	600	1200
Miles jogged	1	2	6	12

So, Elizabeth must run 12 mi ÷ 4.5 mph = about 2.7 h. *Using unit rates:* Find how many calories Elizabeth uses in 1 hour: 4.5 mi × 100 cal = 450 cal/h. Then find the time: 1200 cal ÷ 450 cal/h = about 2.7 h.

Answers to Problem 6.3

Answers will vary. The answers given here will help you evaluate your students' work.

A. Using proportional representation *by regional population only,* we would get the following breakdown (the numbers were computed without rounding the data). (This chart adds to 999 delegates. Students will need to decide how to adjust the numbers to get exactly 1000 delegates. One strategy is to revisit the rounding and see where rounding up makes sense. Other groups may argue to take from a larger region and give to a smaller one.)

Region	Percent	Delegates
New England	$13{,}207 \div 248{,}710 = 5.3\%$	53
Middle Atlantic	$37{,}602 \div 248{,}710 = 15.1\%$	151
East North Central	$42{,}009 \div 248{,}710 = 16.9\%$	169
West North Central	$17{,}660 \div 248{,}710 = 7.1\%$	71
South Atlantic	$43{,}567 \div 248{,}710 = 17.5\%$	175
East South Central	$15{,}176 \div 248{,}710 = 6.1\%$	61
West South Central	$26{,}703 \div 248{,}710 = 10.7\%$	107
Mountain	$13{,}659 \div 248{,}710 = 5.5\%$	55
Pacific	$39{,}127 \div 248{,}710 = 15.7\%$	157

B. If the numbers of delegates from metropolitan areas and from rural areas are to reflect the proportion of each in the United States population, we need to look at this ratio:

$$\frac{\text{population of metro areas}}{\text{U.S. population}} = \frac{\text{delegates from metro areas}}{1000 \text{ delegates}}$$

Then, we can find the rate of persons from metropolitan areas per unit of population. (The numbers in the division are in thousands. Some students may need to see the three zeros on each number to see that they do not affect the rate.)

$$\frac{\text{population of metro areas}}{\text{U.S. population}} = \frac{192{,}726}{248{,}710} = 0.775$$

Multiply the rate by the number of delegates to find the number from metropolitan areas.

$$0.775 \times 1000 = 775 \text{ delegates}$$

The number from rural areas must be $1000 - 775 = 225$ delegates.

C. If the number of delegates of Hispanic origin is to reflect the proportion in the United States population, we need to look at this ratio:

$$\frac{\text{population of Hispanic origin}}{\text{U.S. population}} = \frac{\text{delegates of Hispanic origin}}{1000 \text{ delegates}}$$

Then, we can find the rate of persons of Hispanic origin per unit of population.

$$\frac{\text{population of Hispanic origin}}{\text{U.S. population}} = \frac{22{,}354}{248{,}710} = 0.090$$

Multiply the rate by the number of delegates.

$$0.090 \times 1000 = 90 \text{ delegates}$$

D. Rate calculations similar to those done in parts B and C can be used to find the proportional representation for each racial group.

Race	Rate	Delegates
White	$199{,}686 \div 248{,}710 = 0.803$	803
Black	$29{,}986 \div 248{,}710 = 0.121$	121
Native American–Eskimo–Aleut	$1959 \div 248{,}710 = 0.008$	8
Asian–Pacific Islander	$7274 \div 248{,}710 = 0.029$	29

Adding the four numbers in the right-hand column gives a sum of 961; the difference between this and 1000, or 39, is the number in the category "all other races."

E. Plans will vary.

ACE Answers

Applications

4a. The new distribution of delegates is given in the table.

Region	Area (mi²)	Ratio	Delegates
New England	62,811	$\frac{62,811}{3,536,338} = 0.018$	18
Middle Atlantic	99,463	$\frac{99,463}{3,536,338} = 0.028$	28
East North Central	266,221	$\frac{266,221}{3,536,338} = 0.075$	75
West North Central	243,539	$\frac{243,539}{3,536,338} = 0.069$	69
South Atlantic	178,615	$\frac{178,615}{3,536,338} = 0.051$	51
East South Central	507,981	$\frac{507,981}{3,536,338} = 0.144$	144
West South Central	426,234	$\frac{426,234}{3,536,338} = 0.121$	121
Mountain	856,121	$\frac{856,121}{3,536,338} = 0.242$	242
Pacific	895,353	$\frac{895,353}{3,536,338} = 0.253$	253
Total	3,536,338		1001

Students will have to adjust their distribution if their total is under or over 1000.

Extensions

12a, b.

Student (initials)	People in household	Water use (gallons)	Rate of water use (gallons/person)
RE	5	1901	380.2
TW	4	1682	420.5
HW	5	1493	298.6
WE	4	1336	334.0
GK	5	1332	266.4
DJ	6	1309	218.2
MJ	5	1231	246.2
WD	5	1231	246.2
MA	5	1204	240.8
LR	5	1031	206.2
FP	4	986	246.5
HA	5	985	197.0
TB	3	940	313.3
CH	5	938	187.6
ME	4	924	231.0
JW	4	910	227.5
PR	4	843	210.8
NP	3	819	273.0
BH	4	807	201.8
EB	4	755	188.8
PJ	4	726	181.5
HJ	4	641	160.3
HM	3	554	184.7
JZ	2	493	246.5
Overall total	102	25,071	245.8

12h.

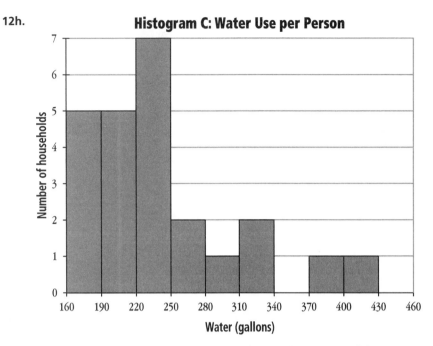

Histogram C: Water Use per Person

Because Histogram A has the smallest intervals, it is the most useful.

Mathematical Reflections

4. If 4 cans feed 6 people, then 160 cans will feed 240 people. You can use a rate table, equivalent ratios ($\frac{4}{6} = \frac{n}{240}$), or divide 240 by 6 to find the number of groups of 6 (there are 40 groups of 6, and $40 \times 4 = 160$ cans). With 45 cans you can feed 67.5 people.

$$\frac{6 \text{ people}}{4 \text{ can}} \times 45 \text{ cans} = \frac{270}{4} \text{ people} = 67.5 \text{ people}$$

5. If you have two measures or counts that you want to compare with the same two kinds of measures or counts in another situation, a ratio comparison takes both numbers into account and gives more information than do differences. For example, suppose you wanted to compare 10 pizzas for 3 people to 15 pizzas for 5 people. The difference of 5 pizzas does not give much information, but $\frac{10}{3}$ pizzas per person compared to $\frac{15}{5}$ pizzas per person is more specific information.

Assigning the Unit Project

The optional unit project provides an opportunity for students to further develop their understanding of ratio and proportion. We recommend that you start the project near the end of the unit (after Investigation 5 or 6).

We recommend that students work on the project with a partner. Each student or pair will need centimeter grid paper; Labsheets UP.A, UP.B, and UP.C; and colored pencils or markers. One class period will be needed for pairs to collect their data. They can continue to investigate the task and draft their reports outside of class. Part of a second class period could be used for comparing results and finalizing reports. You may want to have pairs or individuals share their results in a class summary of the project.

Paper Pool

The project is a mathematical investigation of a new game called Paper Pool. For a pool table, use grid paper rectangles like the one shown at right. Each corner is a pocket where a ball could stop.

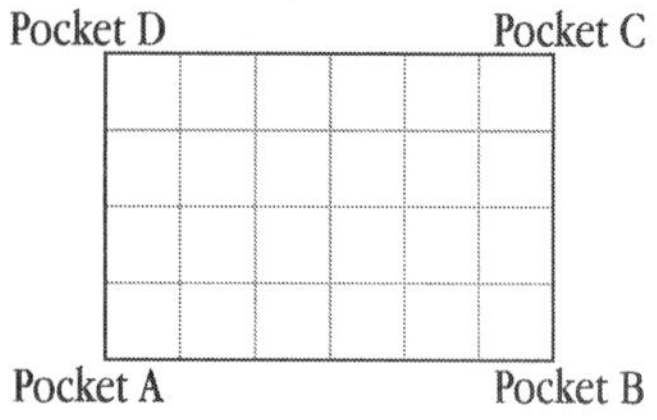

How To Play Paper Pool
- The ball always starts at corner A.
- To start the imaginary ball rolling, hit it with an imaginary cue stick.
- The ball always moves on a 45° diagonal across the grid.
- When the ball hits a side of the table it bounces off at a 45° angle and continues its travel.
- If the ball hits a corner pocket, it falls in and stops.

The dotted lines on the table at the right show the ball's path.

- The ball stopped at corner D.
- It got 5 hits (including the starting hit and the final hit).
- The dimensions of the table are 6 by 4 (always mention the horizontal length first).

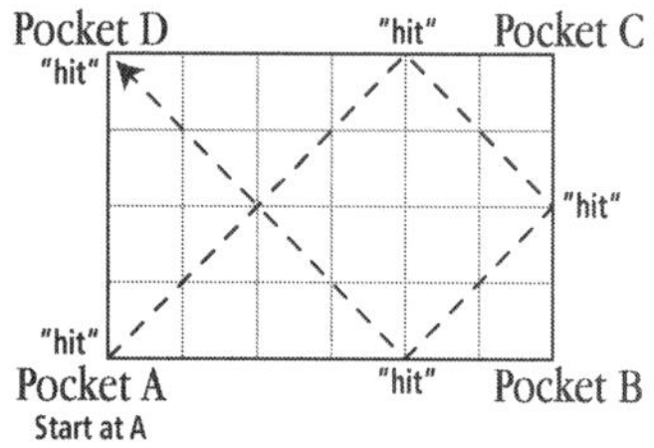

Part 1: Investigate Two Questions

Use Paper Pool Labsheets U.P.A, U.P.B, and U.P.C to play the game. Try to find a rule that tells you (1) the corner where the ball will stop and (2) the number of hits it will make along the way. Keep track of the dimensions because they may give you clues to a pattern.

Part 2: Write a Report

When you find some patterns and reach some conclusions, write a report that includes:

1. A list of the rules you found and why you think they are correct.

2. Drawings of grid paper tables that show your rule.

3. Any tables, charts, or other tools that helped you find patterns.

4. Other patterns or ideas about Paper Pool.

Extension Question

Can you predict the length of the ball's path on any size Paper Pool table? Each time the ball crosses a square, the length is 1 diagonal unit. Find the length of the ball's path in diagonal units for any dimension.

Possible Answers

Using Your Understanding of Proportional Reasoning

1a. The number of students who are bus riders can be compared to the number of students who walk to school in the following ways:

- Look at the difference. How many more students ride the bus than walk to school? In Mr. Archer's room the difference is 5.

- Take the percentage of students who ride the bus and who walk to school. For Mr. Archer's homeroom this is $\frac{20}{35}$ (note that 35 is the total number of students in Mr. Archer's homeroom), or about 57% ride the bus and $\frac{15}{35}$ or about 43% walk to school.

- Look at the ratio (or fraction) of students who ride the bus to the students who walk. In this case it is 15 to 20 or 3 to 4.

- Look at a unit rate or scaling. In this case it is 15 to 20 or 1 walker for about 1.3 bus riders. The number of bus riders is approximately 1.3 times the number of walkers.

Answers continue on page 84a.

Unit Reflections

The problems in this unit all required comparison of measured quantities. In solving those problems you learned when it seems best to use subtraction, division, percents, *rates, ratios,* and *proportions* to make those comparisons. You developed a variety of strategies for writing and solving proportions, including writing *equivalent ratios* to scale a pattern up or down.

Using Your Understanding of Proportional Reasoning—To test your understanding and skill with percents, rates, ratios, and proportions, consider the following problem situations.

(1) *There are 300 students in East Middle School. To plan transportation services for the new West Middle School, the school system surveyed East students to find out how many ride a bus to school and how many walk.*

- In Mr. Archer's homeroom 20 students ride the bus and 15 students walk.

- In Ms. Baker's homeroom 14 students ride the bus and 9 students walk.

- In Ms. Carnick's homeroom 20 students ride the bus and the ratio of bus riders to walkers is 5 to 3.

a. In what ways could you compare the number of students in Mr. Archer's homeroom who are bus riders with the number who are walkers? Which seems the best comparison statement?

b. In what ways could you compare the numbers of bus riders and walkers in Ms. Baker's homeroom with those in the same categories in Mr. Archer's homeroom? Again, which seems the best way to make the comparison?

c. How many students in Ms. Carnick's homeroom walk to school?

d. Based on the information from these three homerooms, how many East Middle School students would you expect to walk to school? To ride a bus?

e. If the new West Middle School will have 450 students and a ratio of bus riders and walkers that is about the same as that in East Middle School, how many West students can be expected in each category?

How to Use
Looking Back and Looking Ahead: Unit Reflections

The first part of this section includes problems that allow students to demonstrate their mathematical understandings and skills. The second part gives them an opportunity to explain their reasoning. This section can be used as a review to help students stand back and reflect on the "big" ideas and connections in the unit. This section may be assigned as homework, followed up with class discussion the next day. Focus on the *Explaining Your Reasoning* section in the discussion. Encourage the students to refer to the problems to illustrate their reasoning.

2 *The Purr & Woof Kennel buys the food shown for the animals that are boarded. The amounts of food eaten by cats, small dogs, and large dogs are as follows:*

Cats: 1/4 pound per day

Small dogs: 1/3 pound per day

Large dogs: 1/2 pound per day

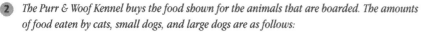

a. Which is cheaper per pound—cat food or dog food?

b. Which is the cheapest to feed—a cat, a small dog, or a large dog?

c. On an average day, the kennel has 20 cats, 30 small dogs, and 20 large dogs.

  i. Which bag of food will last longer—a bag of cat food or a bag of dog food?

  ii. How many bags of dog food and how many bags of cat food will be used in the month of January?

3 *On their way to school Jeff and Tat-Ming saw several stray cats. They decided to do a social studies project on the number of homeless cats. In their research they found that their own town of Centerville has about 100 stray cats, while the neighboring town of Mason has about 60 stray cats. Centerville covers an area of about 12 square miles, and Mason covers about 8 square miles.*

a. Which town has the greater population density of stray cats?

b. How many stray cats would have to move from one town to the other to make the population densities of stray cats in the two towns equal?

4 *Use proportional reasoning to answer the following questions from other* Connected Mathematics *units.*

a. A spinner used in the "Wheel of Destiny" was spun 250 times. The number of wins was 80, and the number of losses was 170. Based on this experience, how many wins would you expect in the next 10 spins?

b. Arnoldo and Bill rode their bikes to soccer practice. Arnoldo rode 7 miles in 25 minutes, and Bill rode 5 miles in 20 minutes. Who rode faster?

1b. Compare percentage of walkers (or bus riders) in Ms. Baker's room to those in Mr. Archer's room. Approximately 57% of students in Mr. Archer's room ride the bus and 43% walk to school. In Ms. Baker's room approximately 61% of the students ride the bus and 39% walk to school.

• Compare ratios of walkers to bus riders in each room. The ratio of bus riders to walkers is 4 to 3 (or $\frac{4}{3}$) in Mr. Archer's room and 14 to 9 (or $\frac{14}{9}$) in Ms. Baker's room.

• Compare unit rates or scaling. In Mr. Archer's room the number of bus riders is approximately 1.3 times the number of walkers. In Ms. Baker's room the number of bus riders is approximately 1.6 times the number of walkers.

• Use the difference between the number of walkers and the difference between the number of bus riders in each room.

  c. 12 students
  The ratio of bus riders to walkers is 5 to 3, the number of riders is 20, and $\frac{5}{3} = \frac{20}{12}$.

1d, e, 2. See page 84b.

3, 4. See page 84c.

Note for the Teacher

Which comparison to use depends on how the information will be used. The difference comparison might be appropriate if a description of the mix is needed. In part a all the riders are paired to walkers, five riders are left over. There is no information about the relative size of each group. Knowing only that the difference is five, the number of walkers compared to riders could be 15 to 20 or 2000 to 2005 or something else. But, differences do not say anything about the relative size of each group. Ratios or scaling are used to compare different quantities relative to each other. In part a the number of bus riders is approximately 1.3 times the number of walkers. Percentages give a relative comparison of each group of students out of the total number of students.

Which comparison to use depends on the intent or question that is being asked.

1d. Expected number of
bus riders: 180
walkers: 120

The total number of walkers in the three homerooms is 36 and the total number of bus riders is 54. The total number of students in the three homerooms is 36 + 54 = 90. The ratio of bus riders to the total number of students in the three homerooms is 54 to 90 or 1 to 1.67. The ratio for the total number of walkers to the total number of students in three homerooms is 36 to 90 or 1 to 2.5. These ratios or rates are used to compute the number of bus riders and walkers for the total student population.

e. Expected number of
bus riders: 270
walkers: 180

2a. cat food: 59.8 cents or about 60 cents per pound dog food: 49 cents per pound. The dog food is cheaper per pound.

b. Each cat costs about 15 cents a day to feed. Each small dog costs about 16 cents per day. Each large dog costs about 24 or 25 cents a day to feed (note that 0.49 ÷ 2 = 0.245). A cat is the cheapest to feed per day.

c. i. a bag of dog food: 20 cats will eat 5 pounds or $\frac{1}{2}$ a sack of cat food per day. The 50 dogs will eat 20 pounds or $\frac{2}{5}$ of a sack of dog food per day. (Each day 30 small dogs eat 30 × $\frac{1}{3}$ pound, and 20 large dogs eat 20 × $\frac{1}{2}$ pound.)

ii. cats: 15.5 bags
.4 bags

84a

. Reflections

---

c. Maria reduced a 100 cm by 150 cm poster by 60%.

   i. What are the dimensions of the new poster?

   ii. How do the perimeter and the area of the new poster compare with the perimeter and the area of the original?

Explaining Your Reasoning—Answering comparison questions often requires knowledge of rates, ratios, percents, and proportional reasoning. As you answer the following questions about your reasoning strategies, use preceding problems and other examples from this unit to illustrate your ideas.

1. How do you decide when it makes sense to compare numbers using ratios, rates, or percents rather than by finding the difference of the two numbers?

2. If you are given information that the ratio of two quantities is 3 to 5, how can you express that relationship in other written forms?

3. The ratio of two quantities is 24 to 18.

   a. State five other equivalent ratios in the form "p to q."

   b. What is the equivalent ratio expressed with smallest possible whole numbers?

4. What strategies could you use to solve proportions such as $\frac{5}{8} = \frac{12}{?}$ and $\frac{5}{8} = \frac{?}{24}$?

5. How does proportional reasoning enter into the solution of problems like these?

   a. You want to prepare enough of your favorite recipe to serve a large crowd.

   b. You want to find the actual distance between two points in a large park from their locations on a map and the scale of the map.

   c. You want to find which package of raisins in a store is the most economical.

   d. You want to use a design drawn on a coordinate grid to make several larger and several smaller copies of that design.

Proportional reasoning is one of the most important ways to compare measured quantities. It gives a way of comparing numerical information by rates and percents. It is also used in geometry to enlarge and reduce figures while retaining their shapes. You will apply proportional reasoning in most of the future *Connected Mathematics* units like *Data Around Us*, *Filling and Wrapping*, *Moving Straight Ahead*, and *What Do You Expect?*

Explaining Your Reasoning

See page 84c.

Looking Back and Looking Ahead

Answers

Using Your Understanding of Proportional Reasoning

3a. The density of cats is about 8.3 cats per square mile in Centerville and about 7.5 cats per square mile in Mason. Centerville has the greater density of cats.

b. To make the densities equal, 4 cats from Centerville must move to Mason.

Note to the Teacher

This problem provides important connections to mathematical concepts that have been studied in prior units.

4a. You would expect to win about 3 times.

b. Arnoldo rode faster. If he rides 7 miles in 25 minutes, then he can ride 28 miles in 100 minutes. If Bill rides 5 miles in 20 minutes, then he can ride 25 miles in 100 minutes. Students might also calculate the speed.

c. i. The dimensions of the new poster are 40 cm by 60 cm.

ii. The perimeter is reduced by 60%. The area is reduced by 36%. ($.60 \times .60$)

Explaining Your Reasoning

1. If a situation has two quantities with different measures, using rates, ratios or percents makes sense. For example, if 10 people share 6 candy bars and another 8 people share 4 candy bars, then the difference is 2 candy bars. But a difference of 2 candy bars does not give much useful information in this situation. But $\frac{6}{10}$ candy bar per person compared to $\frac{4}{8}$ candy bar per person is far more helpful. Another possibility is to use the rate of 1 candy bar per 1.67 people compared to one candy bar per 2 people.

2. 1. 3 to 5 can be written as 1.5 to 2.5, 6 to 10, 30 to 50.

3 to 5 can be written as $\frac{3}{5}, \frac{6}{10}, \frac{30}{50}$.

Percent cannot be used if 3 and 5 are both parts of the same group.

3a. Sample answers: 48 to 36, 72 to 54, 240 to 180, 12 to 9, 4 to 3

b. 4 to 3

4. In the first proportion, find a fraction equivalent to $\frac{5}{8}$ that has a numerator of 12. In the second proportion, a numerator of 15 is produced by rewriting $\frac{5}{8}$ as an equivalent fraction with a denominator of 24. Using equivalent rates is similar to using equivalent fractions.

5a. If the number of people a recipe serves is smaller than the number of people in the crowd, then the recipe must be scaled up to match the crowd.

b. To find the actual distance between two locations, the distance on the map between the two points must be multiplied by the scale factor given on the map. For example, if 1 inch = 100 miles and the map distance is 0.24 inches, then the actual distance is $0.24 \times 100 = 24$ miles.

c. To find the most economical package of raisins, compare the cost per ounce for each brand.

d. To make the design larger, multiply the coordinates of each point by a number greater than 1. To reduce the size of the design, multiply the coordinates of each point by a number less than 1. For example, if the coordinates of the vertices of a triangle are (1, 1), (4, 4) and (6, 2), then an example of a similar, but larger, figure is one whose vertices have coordinates (3, 3), (12, 12) and (18, 6). A smaller similar triangle has vertices with coordinates (0.5, 0.5), (2, 2) and (3, 1). This method is discussed in the *Stretching and Shrinking* unit. This stretching method is similar to scaling up or down.

Assessment
Resources

Check-Up 1

Ms. Sandborn, the student council advisor, is in charge of buying drinks for the school picnic. She conducted a survey that asked students what kind of soft drink they preferred: cola or lemon lime. Here are her results:

Drink Preferences

	Grade 6	Grade 7	Grade 8
Cola	80	75	85
Lemon lime	70	90	80

In 1–4, tell whether the statement is accurate based on the information in the table. Explain your answer.

1. 15 more seventh graders prefer cola to lemon lime.

2. The ratio of seventh graders who prefer cola to lemon lime is 5 to 6.

3. 50% of the students surveyed prefer cola.

4. $\frac{7}{8}$ of the sixth graders prefer lemon lime.

Check-Up 1

5. What percent of students at each grade level prefer lemon lime?

6. What percent of the students surveyed are eighth graders?

7. Write two new correct statements you could make comparing students based on the survey data.

8. Cases of 24 cans of soda usually sell for $6.99. The cases are on sale for $5.94.

    a. What percent savings is this?

    b. What would the price of a case have to be for a buyer to receive a 25% discount?

Check-Up 2

1. So far this year, the University of North Carolina Tar Heels, a college basketball team, has won 22 games and lost 5 games.

   a. Write the ratio of games won to games played.

   b. Write the ratio of games won to games lost.

   c. What percent of their games did the Tar Heels win?

   d. What percent of their games did the Tar Heels lose?

2. Jessica went to her favorite store to buy some bubble gum. The gum is sold in two packages: 5 sticks for 30¢, and 14 sticks for 79¢. Which is the better buy? Why?

3. Driving home, Carmen came to a sign that said traffic would be reduced to one lane for the next 7 miles due to road construction. Cars were only moving at about 5 miles per hour. How long would it take Carmen to get through the construction zone?

4. Ms. Clark's paycheck states that she makes $850.00 a week.

   a. At that rate, how much does she make a year?

   b. Ms. Clark works 40 hours per week. How much does she make an hour?

   c. If 33% of what Ms. Clark makes is deducted for taxes and social security, how much is her net pay (the amount of money for which her check is actually written)?

Quiz

A group of students were planning a picnic for the 30 members of the school newspaper club. They investigated prices for food and drink at two stores and listed their findings in a chart.

Food and Drink Prices

Item	Streamline Market		Bulky Store	
	Quantity	Cost	Quantity	Cost
Punch drink	six 6-ounce bottles per package	$3.00 for 2 packages	36-ounce bottle	$0.69
Cola	six 12-ounce cans	$1.99	twenty-four 12-ounce cans	$6.99
Ground beef (for hamburgers)	1 pound (makes four $\frac{1}{4}$-pound burgers)	$1.39	ten $\frac{1}{4}$-pound patties	$4.99
Hot dogs	1 pound (10 count)	$1.49	2 pounds (20 count)	$2.99
Buns	8-count package	$0.89	12-count package	$1.29
Potato chips	10.5-ounce package	$0.89	40-ounce package	$3.40

1. Which store offers the best buy for punch? Explain how you made your choice.

2. Which store offers the best buy for cola? Explain.

3. How much would it cost to make 30 hamburger patties with ground beef purchased from Streamline?

4. How much would 30 hamburger patties cost at Bulky?

Quiz

5. You need to purchase enough buns to make 30 sandwiches. Buns come in packages of 8 or 12, depending on where you shop. Where would you purchase the buns, and how much would they cost? Explain.

6. Which store offers the best buy for hot dogs? Explain.

7. The students organizing the picnic decided to provide the following for each person attending the picnic:

   • one 12-ounce can of cola
   • 1 hot dog with bun
   • 4 ounces of potato chips

   The school cafeteria donated condiments (mustard, ketchup, relish, and onions), paper plates, and napkins. The students will buy each item at whichever store has the best price. How much should each person attending the picnic pay in order to cover the food expenses? Show how you determined the amount.

Assign these questions as additional homework, or use them as review, quiz, or test questions.

In 1 and 2, use the following data about Lincoln Middle School.

> **Lincoln Middle School**
> Enrollment: 623 students
> Ratio of girls to boys: 2 to 3

1. How many girls are enrolled in Lincoln Middle School?

2. If one teacher is hired for every 25 students enrolled, estimate the number of teachers at Lincoln Middle School.

In 3–8, use the following information on some counties in the United States.

County	State	Population	Land area (square miles)
Bartow	Georgia	61,674	456
Dolores	Colorado	1519	1064
Inyo	California	18,434	10,223
Washington, D.C.	—	570,175	68
Wayne	Michigan	2,064,908	615

Source: *The World Almanac and Book of Facts 1996.* Ed. Robert Famighetti. Mahwah, New Jersey: Funk and Wagnalls, 1995, pp. 428–34.

3. Find the population density for each county listed.

4. Find the population and land area of your county. How does the population density of your county compare to that of the counties in the table?

5. How many times greater is the population of Wayne County than the population of Washington, D.C.?

6. How many times will the land area of Washington, D.C., fit into the land area of Wayne County?

7. What can you say about how Washington, D.C., and Wayne County compare in terms of population and land area?

8. Write two comparison statements about the population densities of the counties in the chart.

9. Kaitlyn wants to estimate how many candies she would get in a 2-pound (32-ounce) bag of chocolate-covered peanuts. She examined several 2-ounce packages of the same candy and counted 8 or 9 candies in each.

   a. How many pieces of candy can Kaitlyn expect to get in a 2-pound bag?

   b. Kaitlyn wants to fill a 64-ounce candy bowl. The 2-ounce bags are sold 8 for $1.00, and the 32-ounce bag costs $2.79. Which is the better buy? Tell how much less it would cost to fill her bowl this way compared to filling it with packages of the other size.

10. Pentominoes Pizza introduced a new pizza called the Giant Foot to compete with Wee Czar's 2-pizzas-for-the-price-of-1 offer. The Giant Foot is two 1-square-foot pizzas put together. Pentominoes' ad claims that the Giant Foot is 25% larger than two Wee Czar's 12-inch round pizzas. A Giant Foot costs $8.99. Two 12-inch round pizzas from Wee Czar's cost $8.88.

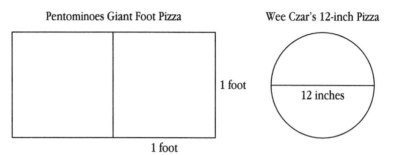

Pentominoes Giant Foot Pizza   Wee Czar's 12-inch Pizza

1 foot

1 foot

12 inches

    a. Which offer gives you more pizza for your money?

    b. Is the Giant Foot 25% larger than two 12-inch round pizzas from Wee Czar's? If so, prove it. If not, use percents to show how they really compare.

11. Which offer is the better buy?

    | 2-liter bottles of Orange Splash! |
    | 4 for $4.99 |

    $\frac{1}{2}$-liter bottles of Orange Splash!
    $1.99 per 8-pack

12. Mr. Seekamp needs several hundred paper clips for a physics experiment. He had some in supply and wants to know whether to order more. Rather than count how many he has stored in a large container, he decides to estimate the number by marking 25 paper clips, replacing them, and randomly drawing out and replacing samples. Here are his sampling results:

    • In a sample of 25 paper clips, 2 were marked.
    • In a sample of 50 paper clips, 5 were marked.

    Based on his two samples, approximately how many paper clips does Mr. Seekamp have?

13. On our planet, land covers 57,900,000 square miles and water covers 139,000,000 square miles.

    a. Write a statement comparing the earth's land surface to its water surface.

    b. What portion of the earth's surface is water?

    c. How does the earth's total surface area compare to your state's area?

14. Leticia is shopping for gifts. She compared prices at two stores so she could get the best deals. For each item, tell which store has the best price.

Gift Prices

Gift	Darren's Warehouse	U-Rule Department Store
handkerchiefs	package of 10 for $11.00	package of 3 for $3.75
greeting cards	package of 8 for $9.99	package of 3 for $5.49
ballpoint pens	one dozen for $9.60	2 for $1.59
audiocassette tapes	one dozen for $13.20	5-pack for $5.95

In 15–17, use the map below.

15. What would be the approximate driving time to travel the United States from coast to coast at an average speed of 55 miles per hour?

16. An airplane averages 500 miles per hour. Choose two cities on the map, and find out how long would it take this plane to fly between them.

17. How far is it from your city to Chihuahua, Mexico?

In 18–21, use the data below. The table shows the all-time top 10 American movies in terms of earnings.

All-Time Top 10 American Movies

Rank	Title (year released)	Earnings (millions)
1	*E.T. The Extra-Terrestrial* (1982)	$399.8
2	*Jurassic Park* (1993)	356.8
3	*Star Wars* (1977)	322.0
4	*The Lion King* (1993)	310.1
5	*Forrest Gump* (1993)	300.6
6	*Home Alone* (1990)	285.5
7	*Return of the Jedi* (1983)	263.0
8	*Jaws* (1975)	260.0
9	*Batman* (1989)	251.2
10	*Raiders of the Lost Ark* (1981)	242.4
	Total earnings	**$2991.4**

Source: *Variety,* Feb. 20–26, 1995, as found in *The World Almanac and Book of Facts 1996.*
Ed. Robert Famighetti. Mahwah, New Jersey: Funk and Wagnalls, 1995, p. 250.

18. How do the earnings of *E.T. The Extra-Terrestrial* and *Raiders of the Lost Ark* compare?

19. Write a fraction that compares the earnings between *Forrest Gump* to the total earnings from the top 10 movies.

20. Write a ratio that compares the earnings of *Jurassic Park* to *Batman*.

21. Write a decimal that compares the earnings of *Star Wars* to the total earnings from the top 10 movies.

In 22–24, use the data in the chart, which shows the population of some counties in the United States.

Selected Counties with Populations over 1 Million

County	State	1990 Population	1994 Population
Los Angeles	California	8,863,052	9,149,840
Harris	Texas	2,818,101	3,045,212
Maricopa	Arizona	2,122,101	2,346,610
Kings	New York	2,300,664	2,271,000
Wayne	Michigan	2,111,687	2,064,908
King	Washington	1,507,305	1,587,505
New York	New York	1,487,536	1,506,430
Cuyahoga	Ohio	1,412,140	1,403,239
Broward	Florida	1,255,531	1,382,983
Allegheny	Pennsylvania	1,336,449	1,320,704

Source: Bureau of the Census, as found in *The World Almanac and Book of Facts 1996.*
Ed. Robert Famighetti. Mahwah, New Jersey: Funk and Wagnalls, 1995, p. 388.

22. How does the population for Los Angeles in 1990 and 1994 compare?

23. Which county had the greatest increase in population from 1990 to 1994? What was the increase?

24. Which counties had a decrease in population from 1990 to 1994? Write the decreased amounts as percents.

In 25–27, use these data about planets in our solar system.

Planet	Average distance from Sun (millions of miles)	Diameter at equator (miles)	Time to circle the Sun	Time to turn on axis
Mercury	36	3032	88 days	59 days
Venus	67	7519	225 days	243 days
Earth	93	7926	365 days	23 hours 56 minutes
Mars	142	4194	687 days	24 hours 37 minutes
Jupiter	484	88,736	11.9 years	9 hours 56 minutes
Saturn	887	74,978	29.5 years	10 hours 40 minutes
Uranus	1784	32,193	84 years	16 hours 48 minutes
Neptune	2796	30,775	165 years	16 hours
Pluto	3666	1423	248 years	6 days 9 hours

Source: *The 1996 Information Please Almanac.* Ed. Otto Johnson. New York: Houghton Mifflin, 1995, p. 331.

25. Write a statement comparing the time it takes for the various planets to circle the Sun.

26. Write a statement comparing the time it takes for the planets to turn on their axes.

27. Mr. Martinelli's science class wants to make a scale model of the universe for the science fair. They need to make some calculations before building their model.

   a. The diameter of the sun is 865,000 miles. If the class made Earth's diameter = 1 inch, what would be the diameter of the scale model of the Sun?

   b. If they made Earth's diameter = 1 inch, what would be the diameter of the scale model of Jupiter?

   c. If they made Earth's diameter = 1 inch, what would be the diameter of the scale model of Pluto?

   d. If the class placed the planets by using a scale of 1 inch = 1 million miles, how many feet from the Sun would the model of Mercury have to be placed?

   e. Using the scale 1 inch = 1 million miles, how far from the Sun would the model of Earth have to be placed?

   f. Using the scale 1 inch = 1 million miles, how far from the Sun would the model of Pluto have to be placed?

Unit Test

1. A jar of 1000 jelly beans was placed in the school's office window.

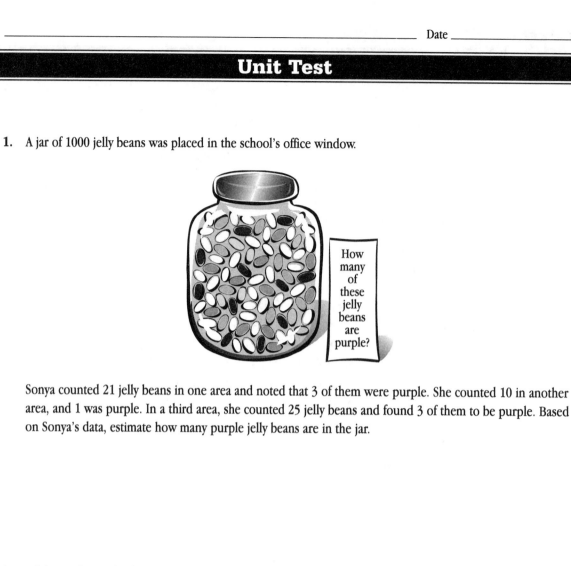

How many of these jelly beans are purple?

Sonya counted 21 jelly beans in one area and noted that 3 of them were purple. She counted 10 in another area, and 1 was purple. In a third area, she counted 25 jelly beans and found 3 of them to be purple. Based on Sonya's data, estimate how many purple jelly beans are in the jar.

2. While watching a hockey match, Tadashi got very thirsty. The snack stand sold drinks in four sizes:

Sorta Swig: 20 ounces for $0.80
Big Swig: 44 ounces for $0.99

Swig: 32 ounces for $0.90
Super Swig: 64 ounces for $1.25

a. Which size would give Tadashi the most refreshment for his money? Explain how you made your decision.

b. If the snack stand offered an 84-ounce Mega Swig, how much should Tadashi expect to pay? Explain your thinking.

Unit Test

In 3–5, use these data about New York and New Mexico.

State	1994 population	Land area (square miles)
New York	18,169,000	47,224
New Mexico	1,654,000	121,364

3. Find the population densities of the two states.

4. How many people would have to move out of New York for it to have the same population density as New Mexico?

5. How many people would have to move from New York to New Mexico for the two states to have the same population density?

6. Adam rode his bike to the library. The 2-mile distance took him about 10 minutes. Adam wondered what his speed was for his trip. Find Adam's speed for the trip in miles per hour.

Name _____ Date _____

Optional Unit Project: Paper Pool

This project is a mathematical investigation of a new game. To complete the project, you will need to collect and organize data as well as find and describe patterns.

Marisa made up a game called Paper Pool. Her "pool tables" were rectangles drawn on grid paper. The "pockets" at each corner were labeled A (lower left), B (lower right), C (upper right), and D (upper left). Marisa always labeled the corners in this order. To the right is one of her Paper Pool tables. Marisa described the size of a table by giving the length of a horizontal side first and the length of a vertical side second. This Paper Pool table is 6 by 4.

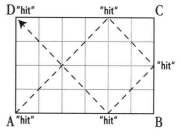

How to Play Paper Pool
- The ball always starts in corner A.
- To start the ball traveling, it is hit with an imaginary cue (a stick for hitting a pool ball).
- The ball always travels at a 45° diagonal across the grid.
- If the ball hits a side of the table, it bounces off at a 45° angle and continues its travel.
- If the ball hits a pocket, it stops.

Marisa played Paper Pool on the table at the right. The dotted line shows the ball's path. On this table, the ball stops at corner D and has a total of 5 hits—one as it was struck by the imaginary cue, three as it bounced off the sides, and one when it stopped at pocket D.

Draw the path the ball would take on the two Paper Pool tables below. For each table, record at what pocket the ball stops, how many hits occurred on its journey, and the dimensions of the table (give the horizontal length first and vertical length second).

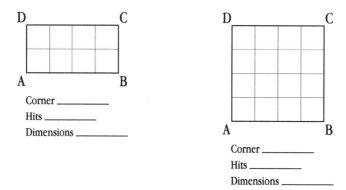

Corner _____
Hits _____
Dimensions _____

Corner _____
Hits _____
Dimensions _____

After playing Paper Pool on tables of several sizes, Marisa wondered whether there is a way to predict the pocket at which the ball will stop and how many hits will have occurred. You will try to answer her questions.

Comparing and Scaling

Optional Unit Project: Paper Pool

Part 1: Investigate Two Questions

Investigate these two questions. Each question is asking you to find out what happens to a ball as it travels on the Paper Pool tables.

1. In what corner will the ball stop?

2. How many hits will have occurred by the time the ball stops?

The Paper Pool tables on Labsheets U.P.A, U.P.B, and U.P.C will help you start thinking about the questions. You may need to draw more tables on grid paper to test your ideas about where the ball will stop and how many hits will have occurred. Review "How to Play Paper Pool" before you start.

When you think you can predict the outcomes, write rules that you could use to determine what will happen to the ball as it travels on a table of any size. Your rules should tell you, *without drawing the path,* the number of hits and the ending corner for the ball.

Part 2: Write a Report

When you have explored several sizes of Paper Pool tables and have reached some conclusions, write a report on your work. Include the following in your report:

1. A summary of the rules you found, why you think your rules are correct, and anything else you discovered. You might discuss what you noticed as you examined the paths for the different tables and what helped you to arrive at your rules.

2. A drawing of one new Paper Pool table (not from the labsheets) for each rule that demonstrates that the rule accurately predicts what will happen.

3. Your drawings of the ball's path on each Paper Pool table on the labsheets as well as any other Paper Pool tables you constructed to help you derive your rules.

4. Any tables, charts, or other schemes or tools you used to organize your information and look for patterns.

5. An explanation of any other patterns you found or ideas you have about Paper Pool tables and the path of the ball. (For example, on which tables does the ball's path follow the same basic course? On which tables does the design created by the ball's path look the same?)

Extension Question

Can you predict the length of the path the ball will travel on *any size* Paper Pool table? Each time the ball crosses a square, the distance it travels is 1 diagonal unit. How many diagonal units will the ball's path cover?

1 diagonal unit

path length = 6 diagonal units

Notebook Checklist

Journal Organization

_____ Problems and Mathematical Reflections are labeled and dated.

_____ Work is neat and is easy to find and follow.

Vocabulary

_____ All words are listed.   _____ All words are defined or described.

Check-Ups and Quiz

_____ Check-Up 1

_____ Check-Up 2

_____ Quiz

Homework Assignments

_____ _____

_____ _____

_____ _____

_____ _____

_____ _____

_____ _____

_____ _____

_____ _____

_____ _____

_____ _____

_____ _____

_____ _____

_____ _____

_____ _____

Self-Assessment

Vocabulary

Of the vocabulary words I defined or described in my journal, the word _____ best demonstrates my ability to give a clear definition or description.

Of the vocabulary words I defined or described in my journal, the word _____ best demonstrates my ability to use an example to help explain or describe an idea.

Mathematical Ideas

In *Comparing and Scaling,* I learned that making useful comparisons of numbers sometimes requires more than just finding which number is larger or smaller. It may require finding and explaining comparisons between quantities that describe or measure a situation.

1. **a.** I learned to compare numbers in several ways: using fractions, percents, ratios, rates, scaling, and differences. These explanations and examples show my understanding of each method:

    b. Here are page numbers of journal entries that give evidence of what I have learned, along with descriptions of what each entry shows:

2. **a.** These are the mathematical ideas I am still struggling with:

    b. This is why I think these ideas are difficult for me:

    c. Here are page numbers of journal entries that give evidence of what I am struggling with, along with descriptions of what each entry shows:

Class Participation

I contributed to the class discussion and understanding of *Comparing and Scaling* when I . . . (Give examples.)

13. **a.** Possible answer: The earth's water surface is about 2.4 times its land surface.

    b. About $\frac{139,000,000}{196,900,000} = 70.6\%$ of the earth's surface is water.

    c. Answers will vary. For example: South Dakota has a total area of 77,121 mi^2, so the earth's surface area is about $196,900,000 \div 77,121 = 2553$ times that of South Dakota's.

14. The table shows the unit price for each item at each store. Darren's has the best unit price on handkerchiefs, greeting cards, and audiocassette tapes; ballpoint pens cost essentially the same at the two stores. (Students may argue that pens are cheaper at U-Rule; a point that should be discussed is that the difference is negligible unless a large quantity is purchased.)

Item	Darren's Warehouse	U-Rule Department Store
handkerchiefs	$1.10	$1.25
greeting cards	1.25	1.83
ballpoint pens	0.80	0.795
audiocassette tapes	1.10	1.19

15. Depending on where the distance is measured, it is about 13.5 cm from coast to coast, or $13.5 \times 195 = 2630$ miles. If there were a direct road, it would take $\frac{2630}{55}$ = about 48 hours to drive from coast to coast. Since there is no direct road, it will take longer.

16. Possible answer: From Seattle to Los Angeles, it is 4.9 cm × 195 mi/cm = about 956 mi, so it would take the plane about $\frac{956}{500}$ = about 2 h.

17. Possible answer: From Columbus, Ohio (near the center of the state), it is about 7.2 cm × 195 mi/cm = 1404 mi to Chihuahua.

18. *E.T.* earned about $\frac{400}{240} = \frac{5}{3}$ or 1.67 times what *Raiders* earned.

19. *Forrest Gump* earned about $\frac{300}{3000}$ or $\frac{1}{10}$ of the total earnings of the top 10 movies.

20. *Jurassic Park* earned about $\frac{350}{250} = \frac{7}{5}$ of the amount earned by *Batman*.

21. *Star Wars* earned about $\frac{322}{2991} = 0.11$ of the total earnings of the top 10 movies.

22. Possible answers: There was an increase of over a quarter of a million people (286,788). As a ratio, there was about a $\frac{286,788}{8,863,052} = 3.2\%$ increase.

23. The population of Maricopa County increased by $\frac{224,509}{2,122,101}$ = about 10.6%.

24. Kings County had a 1.3% decrease, Wayne County had a 2.2% decrease, Cuyahoga County had a 0.6% decrease, and Allegheny County had a 1.2% decrease.

25. Possible answer: Planets closer to the sun take less time to circle the sun. Some take less than 1 year, while others take more than 100 years.

26. Possible answer: Earth and Mars take about the same amount of time to turn on their axes.

27. **a.** Sun's diameter: $\frac{865,000}{7926}$ = about 109 in

    b. Jupiter's diameter: $\frac{88,736}{7926}$ = about 11.2 in

    c. Pluto's diameter: $\frac{1423}{7926}$ = about 0.18 in

    d. Mercury: $\frac{36}{12} = 3$ ft

    e. Earth: $\frac{93}{12} = 7.75$ ft

    f. Pluto: $\frac{3666}{12} = 306$ ft

Answer Keys

Answers to the Unit Test

1. Sonya counted a total of 56 jelly beans, 7 of which were purple, which is $\frac{7}{56} = 12.5\%$ of the jelly beans. Since 12.5% of 1000 = 125, there are about 125 purple jelly beans in the jar.

2. a. Sorta Swig: $\frac{20\ oz}{\$0.80} = 25$ oz per dollar; Swig: $\frac{32\ oz}{\$0.90} =$ about 36 oz per dollar; Big Swig: $\frac{44\ oz}{\$0.99} =$ about 44 oz per dollar; Super Swig: $\frac{64\ oz}{\$1.25} =$ about 51 oz per dollar. The Super Swig would give Tadashi the most for his money.

   b. Possible answer: At the rate of the Super Swig, the Mega Swig would cost $\frac{\$1.25}{64\ oz} \times 84$ oz = \$1.64. However, since the larger sizes offer more for the money, the Mega Swig may have a better rate, such as 60 oz per dollar. At that rate, the Mega Swig would cost $\frac{\$1.00}{60\ oz} \times 84$ oz = \$1.40. (Other answers are possible, as long as students justify their answer mathematically.)

3. New York: $\frac{18,169,000}{47,224} = 384.7$ people per mi^2; New Mexico: $\frac{1,654,000}{121,364} = 13.6$ people per mi^2

4. For New York to have New Mexico's population density of 13.6 people per mi^2, there could be only $13.6 \times 47,224 = 642,246$ people in New York. That means that $18,169,000 - 642,246 = 17,526,754$ people would have to move from New York.

5. Possible answer: The overall population density is

   $$\frac{18,169,000 + 1,654,000}{47,224 + 121,364} = \text{about } 117.6 \text{ people per } mi^2$$

   New York's new population would have to be

   $$117.6 \times 47,224 = 5,553,542 \text{ people}$$

   To achieve this, $18,169,000 - 5,553,542 = 12,615,458$ people would have to move from New York to New Mexico. (There are several ways this problem can be solved. A guess-and-check method can be time-consuming but does offer an opportunity to see how students are reasoning.)

6. An equivalent rate for $\frac{2\ miles}{10\ min}$ is $\frac{12\ miles}{60\ min}$, which equals $\frac{12\ miles}{1\ hr}$, for a rate of 12 mph.

The optional Unit Project provides an opportunity for students to further develop their understanding of ratio and proportion. This section contains preparation notes for the Paper Pool project, answers, and a holistic-by-category scoring rubric with guidelines for how it can be used to assess the project. Samples of two students' work and a teacher's comments accompany the suggested rubric.

Preparing for the Paper Pool Project

In the project, students are asked to play a game called Paper Pool. The game is played on rectangular square-grid tables, such as the one shown here.

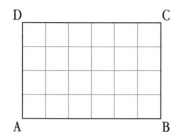

An imaginary ball is hit from the lower left-hand corner (labeled A) at a 45° angle. A ball hit in this way will bounce off each side it hits at a 45° angle. The ball continues to roll until it encounters a pocket. Pockets are located at each corner.

Students are asked to predict in which pocket the ball will stop and how many hits (anything making contact with the ball—the sides of the table, the imaginary cue, or a pocket—counts as a hit) will occur by the time the ball comes to a stop (reaches a pocket). To do this, students will need to investigate several Paper Pool table sizes. Finding a solution will require them to recognize relationships between rectangles whose sides have the same ratio. The goals of the project are for students

- to gather and organize data
- to search for patterns
- to recognize rectangles with sides in the same ratio (similar rectangles)
- to use the simplest ratio to predict the stopping pocket and the number of hits

We recommend that you start the project near the end of the unit (after Investigation 5 or 6). Distribute the Unit Project handout, and review the task introduction with your students. Make sure they understand how the ball travels on the Paper Pool tables and how to count the number of hits that occur on any table. Check that they have drawn the paths correctly for the two sample tables.

An extension question is offered with this task. You may want to assign it to everyone or use it as an extra challenge for groups who want to investigate patterns further.

We recommend that students work on this project with a partner. Each student or pair will need centimeter grid paper; Labsheets U.P.A, U.P.B, and U.P.C; and colored pencils or markers. One class period will be needed for pairs to collect their data. They can continue to investigate the task and draft their reports outside of class. Part of a second class period could be used for comparing results and finalizing reports. You may want to have pairs or individuals share their results in a class summary of the project. If the extension question was given as an extra challenge, be sure to ask any pair who attempted it to share their answers.

Answers to the Paper Pool Project

The Paper Pool project is an open-ended investigation, with a wide range of possible observations that students could make. In the project, students are asked to find patterns and write rules about how the ball travels on Paper Pool tables.

Some students may give rules that are related to a specific example, while others may give rules that generalize across several different rectangles. In the examples below, we call a rule that works for all tables with a specific characteristic in common (such as a horizontal length of 1 and a vertical length that is an even number) a "specific" rule. Rules that look beyond a single common characteristic and apply to a more general category we call "sophisticated" rules.

Possible Rules for Predicting the Stopping Corner

Specific rules (usually involves only one variable)

- If the table is a square, the ball will stop at corner C.
- If the table has a *horizontal dimension* of 1 unit and a *vertical dimension* that is an odd number, the ball will stop at corner C.
- If the table has a *horizontal dimension* of 1 unit and a *vertical dimension* that is an even number, the ball will stop at corner D.
- If the table has a *vertical dimension* of 1 unit and a *horizontal dimension* that is an odd number, the ball will stop at corner C.
- If the table has a *vertical dimension* of 1 unit and a *horizontal dimension* that is an even number, the ball will stop at corner B.
- The ball will never stop at corner A.
- In all similar rectangles of the same orientation, the ball will stop at the same corner.

Sophisticated rules (compares more than one variable)
In all similar rectangles of the same orientation, the ball will stop at the same corner. The corner is determined by the ratio of table's sides. If the ratio of the horizontal dimension to the vertical dimension is

- an odd number to an odd number, the ball will stop at corner C.
- an odd number to an even number, the ball will stop at corner D.
- an even number to an odd number, the ball will stop at corner B.

Possible Rules for Predicting the Number of Hits

Specific rules (usually involves only one variable)

- If the table is a square, there will be two hits.
- If the table has a side length of 1, the number of hits will be 1 greater than the length of the other side (or, the number of hits will be the sum of the two sides).
- For all similar rectangles, the number of hits is the same.

Sophisticated rules (compares more than one variable)

For all similar rectangles, the number of hits is the same. The number of hits is the sum of the numbers of the simplified ratio (to lowest whole-number amounts) of the table's sides.

Extension Question

The length of the path traveled by the ball is the least common multiple of the numbers that are the dimensions of the table.

Suggested Scoring Rubric

This rubric employs a point scale for four different areas of assessment for a total of 21 possible points. (The rubric does not assess students' work on the optional extension question.) Use the rubric as presented here, or modify it to fit your needs and your district's requirements for evaluating and reporting students' work and understanding.

Mathematics *(8 points possible)*
Rules or patterns for predicting the stopping corner (0–4 points)

4   Student states at least one correct sophisticated rule and addresses all possible situations for where the ball will stop.

3   Student states one correct sophisticated rule or several specific rules that address several possible situations for where the ball will stop.

2   Student states at least two correct specific rules.

1   Student shows evidence of searching for a pattern but states no original pattern or rule *or* student states one specific rule.

0   Student does not engage; gives no patterns or rules.

Rules or patterns for predicting the number of hits (0–4 points)

4   Student states at least one correct sophisticated rule and addresses all possible situations for the number of hits.

3   Student states one correct sophisticated rule or several specific rules that address several possible situations for the number of hits.

2   Student states at least two correct specific rules.

1   Student shows evidence of searching for a pattern but states no original pattern or rule *or* student states one correct specific rule.

0   Student does not engage; gives no patterns or rules.

Problem Solving and Reasoning *(4 points possible)*

4   Student shows complete reasoning to support sophisticated rules for both situations.

3   Student shows adequate reasoning to support at least one sophisticated rule *or* student gives complete reasoning to support specific rules for both situations.

2   Student shows reasoning about rules through words or organizational instruments but the reasoning is weak—it tests an inadequate variety of situations and draws conclusions that would require testing more cases or examining more varied arrangements *or* student has only one or two specific rules and does not address both situations.

1   Student shows reasoning about rules through words or organizational instruments but the reasoning is faulty—it employs incorrect logic or nonsensical statements in the context of the problem *or* student only reasons through one specific rule.

0   Student does not engage in the task.

Communication *(4 points possible)*

4   Report is clearly written and easy to follow.

3   With some extra effort, the reader can follow the student's report.

2   Significant effort is needed to follow the student's report.

1   Student does not address the task.

0   Student does not communicate in any form.

Checklist *(5 points possible)*

2   Student gives a correct new table for each rule and gives at least two rules. (One rule and one correct corresponding table is worth 1 point.)

2   Students uses organizational tool(s) to search for patterns and rules. (Quality is the determining factor for giving a paper 0, 1, or 2 points.)

1   Student completes Labsheets U.P.A, U.P.B, and U.P.C.

A Teacher's Comments

I had students work in pairs, but each wrote their own report. I used the suggested schedule, one class period and then half a class period three days later. This allowed students who needed more time to investigate the situation and look for patterns to do so at home. The half period was used to discuss and revise reports as partners shared what they had written. Most of my students found this project interesting and were very engaged in the mathematical investigation.

The students' reports came in several forms and levels of quality. Shown below are examples of student work from the class (the students' labsheets and any additional drawings they did are not included). The work was scored using the suggested rubric.

Guide to the Optional Unit Project

Sample Student Work

> Mary Beth
>
> We discovered that before you can really find rules you have to convert the paper pool tables into basic tables, or smallest form. As we did that we realized that there would be no even by even dimensions because they can be broken down. The possible dimensions are odd by odd, odd by even, and even by odd. Odd by even and even by odd dimensions are different because the pockets would be in different corners. The odd by odd dimensions always end in the C pocket, odd by even in B, and even by odd in D. To find how many hits there will be, add the dimensions. The total will also include the starting and finishing pockets.

Mary Beth's project received 8 of the 8 possible points for the mathematics in her report. A 4 was given for her sophisticated rule on which corner the ball would stop. Her rule for the stopping corner covers all possible cases. She notes that it makes a difference whether the table is odd by even or even by odd, but she does not tell whether she is giving the horizontal dimension or the vertical dimension first. Her drawings and organizational tools (she made tables to organize her information) made it possible to determine what she meant, so full credit for her rules was given. A 4 was given for her sophisticated rule for the number of hits that would occur. Her rule identifies the sum of the dimensions of the table as the important relationship, but her written report does not state that it is the sum of the dimensions *when expressed as a ratio in simplest form* (or what she calls earlier "basic" form). I might have counted down for this if it were not for the fact that her labsheets, new drawings, and organizational tools showed that she understood this.

Mary Beth received a score of 4 for problem solving and reasoning. When her written summary, new drawings, and organizational tools are taken into account, her reasoning for her rules is complete. She received only 3 points for communication because of the effort the reader needs to make to sort out which side she is referring to in her odd-by-even and even-by-odd rules, and because of the lack of clarity and completeness in her written description of her rule for the stopping corner.

Mary Beth's new table, labsheet, and organizational tool were included in her report and she was given all the points for this section due to their quality and completeness. She received a total of 20 out of the 21 points and was given an A.

Heather's project received 5 of the 8 points for the mathematics in her report. A 3 was given for six basic rules and one sophisticated rule that identifies the stopping corner. A 2 was given for her three basic rules for the number of hits (a fourth rule for "two hits" was started but not completed). Her rules for the stopping corner cover several possibilities, and her rule of "On an odd by odd it will always end up at corner C" is considered a sophisticated rule. She does not address the orientation of the rectangle, and the reader can only make sense of her rules by examining her drawings and organizational tools. Heather's rules for stopping corner suggest that she looked for patterns. Her rules for the number of hits are part of some of her rules for stopping corners. The count she gives for the number of hits is incorrect and suggests that she does not understand what counts as a hit. It seems that she has not counted the hit from the cue nor the hit at the last pocket.

> **Heather**
>
> * For a 1 by any odd number it will end up at C.
> * For a 1 by any even number it will end up at B.
> * If one side is twice as big as the other side it will hit once & end up at B.
> * When it is a square it will not hit a side, but go to diagonal corner C.
> * On an odd by odd it will always end up at corner C & hit as many times as possibal.
> * If 1 demention is 4x larger or ¼ the other, it hits 3 times & lands in B.
> * Nothing ends up in A.

Because Heather shows no evidence of being able to reason about how many hits will occur, and because the reader's only evidence of her reasoning is through her labsheets and single organizational chart, she was given a 2 for problem solving and reasoning. A 2 was given for communication, because the reader must make a significant effort to follow her report. Because Heather does not deal with the orientation of the rectangles, one must make an effort to sort through her work and make sense of the rules she has given.

Heather's new tables to demonstrate her rules were complete, and she received 2 points for them. Her labsheets were also complete; she received the 1 point for including these. She received 1 point for her organizational tools, which included only a table that organized the information about the stopping corner. She did not include an organizational tool addressing the number of hits.

Heather received 13 of 21 points and a grade of C. Her labsheets show that she is not counting hits correctly. I'm not sure why this is, because when we launched the project in class, both she and her partner correctly counted the number of hits for the sample Paper Pool tables. Further instruction will probably be needed to help the partners address the issue of hits. I will also want to talk to Heather and all the students about how to look for patterns and how to organize information to help in looking for patterns.

The teacher writes the problem on the board in long-division notation.

$$5\overline{)\$29.95}$$

Teacher: And if I want to divide the $29 equally into 5 groups, how much would go to each group?
Cherise: $5 for each group.
Teacher: How much would that use of the $29?
Cherise: $25, and you would have $4 left.

The teacher continues to record what is being said.

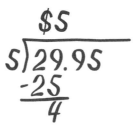

Teacher: If we have $4 left, we can't give each of the 5 groups another dollar, so what would you do?
Brenda: Make the $4 into 40 dimes, and with the 90¢, that makes 49 dimes.

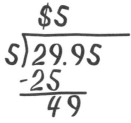

Teacher: If we divide the 49 dimes among the 5 groups, how many dimes would each group get?
Brenda: Nine, and there would be 4 dimes left over.

$$
\begin{array}{r}
\$5.9 \\
5\overline{)29.95} \\
\underline{-25} \\
49 \\
\underline{-45} \\
4
\end{array}
$$

Blackline Masters

U.S. Census Data

U.S. 1990 Population by Region, Race, and Metro/Rural Location (All Numbers in 1000s)

	Total	Metro areas	Rural areas	White	Black	Hispanic*	Native American, Eskimo, Aleut	Asian, Pacific Islander
United States	**248,710**	**192,726**	**55,984**	**199,686**	**29,986**	**22,354**	**1959**	**7274**
New England	**13,207**	**10,598**	**2609**	**12,033**	**628**	**568**	**33**	**232**
Maine	1228	441	787	1208	5	7	6	7
New Hampshire	1109	622	487	1087	7	11	2	9
Vermont	563	131	431	555	2	4	2	3
Massachusetts	6016	5438	578	5405	300	288	12	143
Rhode Island	1003	928	75	917	39	46	4	18
Connecticut	3287	3038	250	2859	274	213	7	51
Middle Atlantic	**37,602**	**34,193**	**3409**	**30,036**	**4986**	**3186**	**92**	**1104**
New York	17,990	16,386	1605	13,385	2859	2214	63	694
New Jersey	7730	7730	n/a	6130	1037	740	15	273
Pennsylvania	11,882	10,077	1805	10,520	1090	232	15	137
East North Central	**42,009**	**32,557**	**9452**	**35,764**	**4817**	**1438**	**150**	**573**
Ohio	10,847	8567	2280	9522	1155	140	20	91
Indiana	5544	3796	1748	5021	432	99	13	38
Illinois	11,431	9450	1981	8953	1694	904	22	285
Michigan	9295	7446	1850	7756	1292	202	56	105
Wisconsin	4892	3298	1593	4513	245	93	39	54
West North Central	**17,660**	**10,132**	**7528**	**16,254**	**899**	**289**	**188**	**195**
Minnesota	4375	2960	1415	4130	95	54	50	78
Iowa	2777	1223	1554	2683	48	33	7	25
Missouri	5117	3387	1730	4486	548	62	20	41
North Dakota	639	257	381	604	4	5	26	3
South Dakota	696	205	491	638	3	5	51	3
Nebraska	1578	766	812	1481	57	37	12	12
Kansas	2478	1333	1145	2232	143	94	22	32
South Atlantic	**43,567**	**32,461**	**11,106**	**33,391**	**8924**	**2133**	**172**	**631**
Delaware	666	442	224	535	112	16	2	9
Maryland	4781	4439	343	3394	1190	125	13	140
District of Columbia	607	607	n/a	180	400	33	1	11
Virginia	6187	4483	1704	4792	1163	160	15	159
West Virginia	1793	653	1140	1726	56	8	2	7
North Carolina	6629	3758	2871	5008	1456	77	80	52
South Carolina	3487	2113	1374	2407	1040	31	8	22
Georgia	6478	4212	2266	4600	1747	109	13	76
Florida	12,938	11,754	1184	10,749	1760	1574	36	154

	Total	Metro areas	Rural areas	White	Black	Hispanic*	Native American, Eskimo, Aleut	Asian, Pacific Islander
East South Central	**15,176**	**8513**	**6663**	**12,049**	**2977**	**95**	**41**	**84**
Kentucky	3685	1714	1971	3392	263	22	6	18
Tennessee	4877	3300	1577	4048	778	33	10	32
Alabama	4041	2723	1317	2976	1021	25	17	22
Mississippi	2576	776	1798	1633	915	16	9	13
West South Central	**26,703**	**19,614**	**7,089**	**20,142**	**3929**	**4539**	**350**	**407**
Arkansas	2351	943	1408	1945	374	20	13	13
Louisiana	4220	2935	1285	2839	1299	93	19	41
Oklahoma	3146	1870	1276	2584	234	86	252	34
Texas	16,987	13,867	3119	12,775	2022	4340	66	319
Mountain	**13,659**	**9179**	**4480**	**11,762**	**374**	**1992**	**481**	**217**
Montana	799	191	608	741	2	12	48	4
Idaho	1007	206	801	950	3	53	14	9
Wyoming	454	134	319	427	4	26	9	3
Colorado	3294	2686	608	2905	133	424	28	60
New Mexico	1515	733	782	1146	30	579	134	14
Arizona	3665	2896	769	2963	111	688	204	55
Utah	1723	1336	387	1616	12	85	24	33
Nevada	1202	996	206	1013	79	124	20	38
Pacific	**39,127**	**35,479**	**3648**	**28,255**	**2454**	**8114**	**453**	**3831**
Washington	4867	3976	891	4309	150	215	81	211
Oregon	2842	1947	895	2637	46	113	38	69
California	29,760	28,493	1267	20,524	2209	7688	242	2846
Alaska	550	226	324	415	22	18	86	20
Hawaii	1108	836	272	370	27	81	5	685

* Persons of Hispanic origin may be of any race.

Totals include other races, which are not shown separately. N/A means not applicable.

Source: *Statistical Abstract of the United States 1993.* Published by the Bureau of the Census, Washington, D.C., p. 254.

ACE Question 12

Student (initials)	People in household	Water use (gallons)	Rate of water use (gallons/person)	Rate of water use (gallons/person) (rounded to nearest 10)
RE	5	1901		
TW	4	1682		
HW	5	1493		
WE	4	1336		
GK	5	1332		
DJ	6	1309		
MJ	5	1231		
WD	5	1231		
MA	5	1204		
LR	5	1031		
FP	4	986		
HA	5	985		
TB	3	940		
CH	5	938		
ME	4	924		
JW	4	910		
PR	4	843		
NP	3	819		
BH	4	807		
EB	4	755		
PJ	4	726		
HJ	4	641		
HM	3	554		
JZ	2	493		
Overall total				

Paper Pool Tables 1

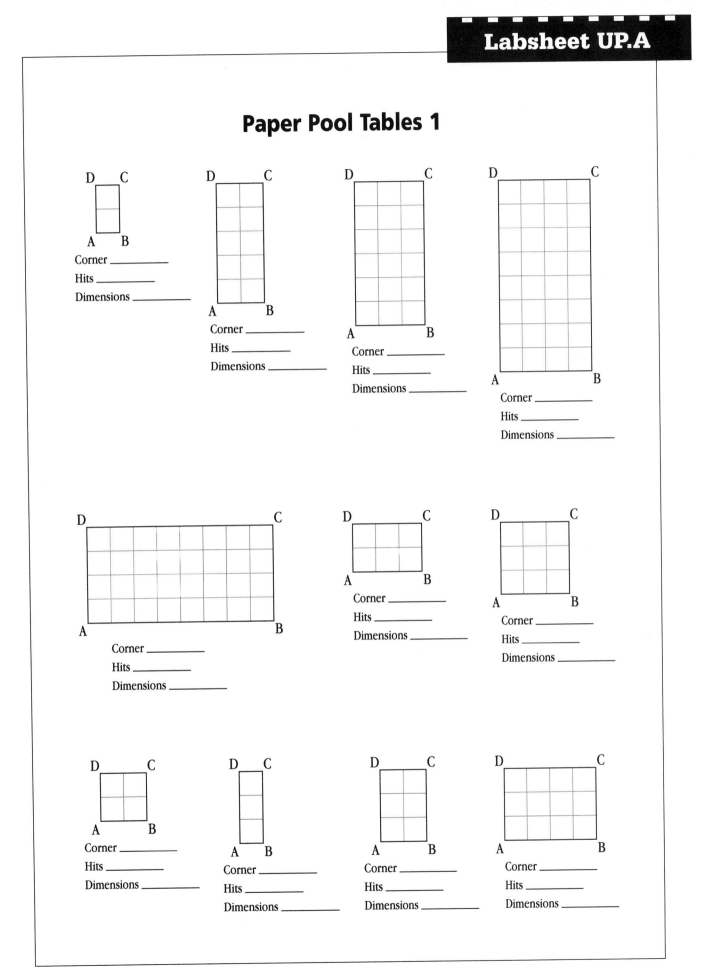

D   C

A   B

Corner _____

Hits _____

Dimensions _____

D   C

A   B

Corner _____

Hits _____

Dimensions _____

D   C

A   B

Corner _____

Hits _____

Dimensions _____

D   C

A   B

Corner _____

Hits _____

Dimensions _____

D   C

A   B

Corner _____

Hits _____

Dimensions _____

D   C

A   B

Corner _____

Hits _____

Dimensions _____

D   C

A   B

Corner _____

Hits _____

Dimensions _____

D   C

A   B

Corner _____

Hits _____

Dimensions _____

D   C

A   B

Corner _____

Hits _____

Dimensions _____

D   C

A   B

Corner _____

Hits _____

Dimensions _____

D   C

A   B

Corner _____

Hits _____

Dimensions _____

Paper Pool Tables 2

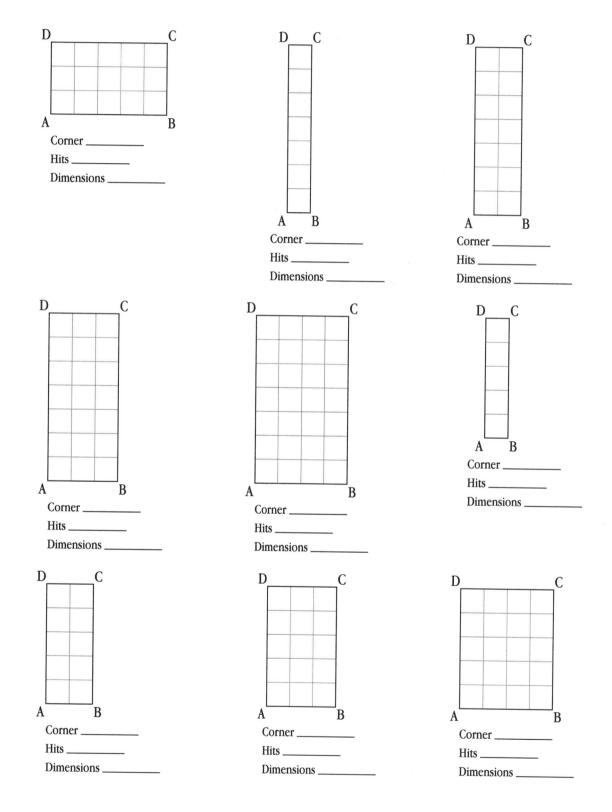

Corner _____

Hits _____

Dimensions _____

Corner _____

Hits _____

Dimensions _____

Corner _____

Hits _____

Dimensions _____

Corner _____

Hits _____

Dimensions _____

Corner _____

Hits _____

Dimensions _____

Corner _____

Hits _____

Dimensions _____

Corner _____

Hits _____

Dimensions _____

Corner _____

Hits _____

Dimensions _____

Corner _____

Hits _____

Dimensions _____

Comparing and Scaling

Paper Pool Tables 3

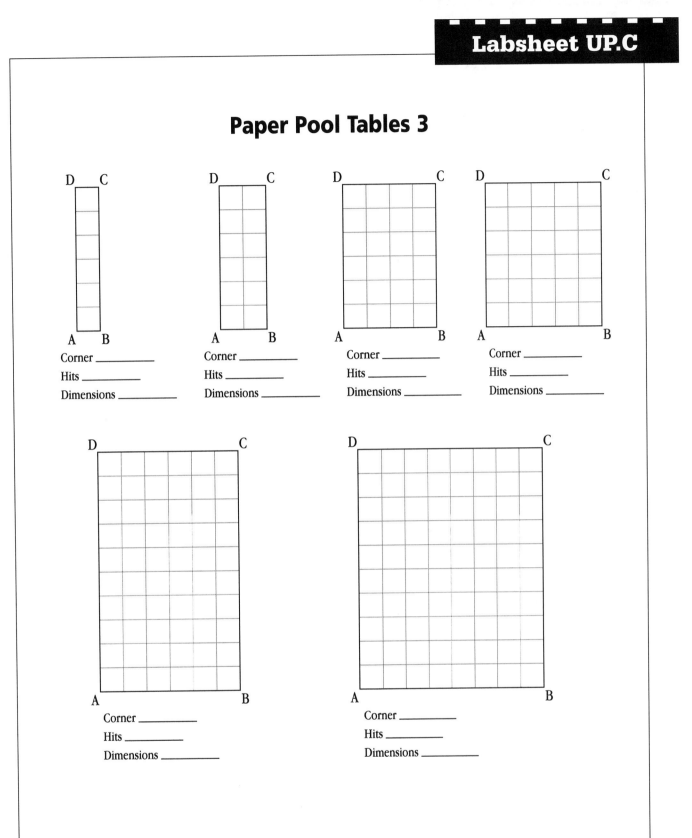

Corner _____

Hits _____

Dimensions _____

Corner _____

Hits _____

Dimensions _____

Corner _____

Hits _____

Dimensions _____

Corner _____

Hits _____

Dimensions _____

Corner _____

Hits _____

Dimensions _____

Corner _____

Hits _____

Dimensions _____

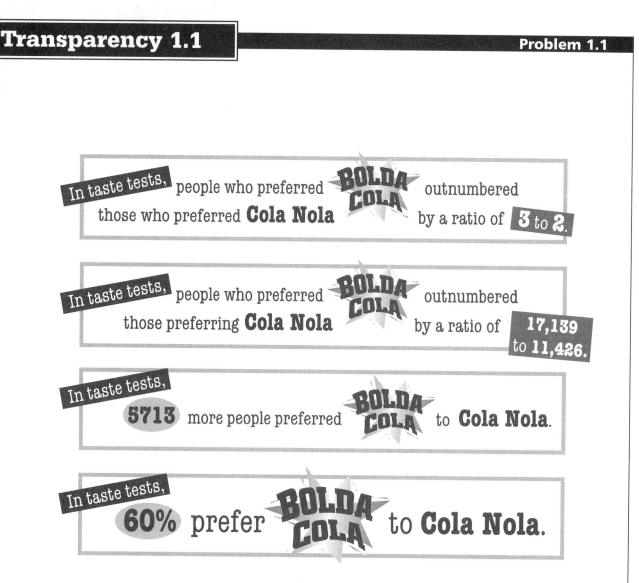

A. Describe what you think each of the four statements means. Explain how each shows a comparison. Be sure to tell *what* is being compared and *how* it is being compared.

B. Is it possible that all four advertising claims are based on the same survey data? Explain your answer.

C. Which comparison do you think is the most accurate way to report the survey data? Why?

D. Which comparison do you think would be the most effective advertisement for Bolda Cola? Why?

1. 6 out of 10 students prefer television to radio.

2. Students prefer radio to television by a ratio of 4 to 6.

3. Students who prefer television outnumber those who prefer radio by 20.

4. Students who prefer television outnumber those who prefer radio by a ratio of 3 to 2.

5. The number of students who prefer watching television is 1.5 times the number who prefer listening to radio.

6. 40% of the students prefer radio to television.

7. $\frac{3}{5}$ of the students prefer television to radio.

A survey of 100 students at Neilson Middle School found that 60 students prefer watching television in the evening and 40 prefer listening to the radio.

A. Read the statements about how Neilson students prefer to spend their evenings. Tell whether each statement accurately reports the results of the survey. Explain your answers.

B. If you were writing a paper to convince local merchants that they would reach more students by advertising on the radio than on television, which statement would you use? Why?

C. Imagine that you are the advertising director for a television station in the town where Neilson is located. You have been asked to prepare a report for a meeting between your ad department and a large local skateboard manufacturer. Which statement would you use to try to convince the manufacturer to advertise on your station? Why?

Camping Data

	Ages 12–17	Ages 18–24	Ages 25–34
Total in the age group	21,304,000	26,650,000	41,808,000
Number who camp at least twice a year	5,336,000	4,767,000	10,000,000

Source: National Sporting Goods Association, as found in the *Statistical Abstract of the United States 1995*. Published by the Bureau of the Census, Washington, D.C., p. 260.

Suppose you were asked to write a news story about the popularity of camping in the United States based on the data in the table.

A. What headline would you use for your story? What would your first sentence be?

B. Write five statements you could use in your story to compare the popularity of camping among people in the three age groups. In each statement, be clear about which groups you are comparing. Your comparisons should be specific and based on mathematics.

Participation in Sports Activities

Activity	Males	Females	Ages 12–17	Ages 55–64
Bicycle riding	24,562,000	23,357,000	8,794,000	2,030,000
Camping	23,165,000	19,533,000	5,336,000	2,355,000
Exercise walking	21,054,000	43,373,000	2,816,000	7,782,000
Fishing	30,449,000	14,885,000	4,945,000	3,156,000
Swimming	27,713,000	33,640,000	10,874,000	2,756,000
Total in group	**111,851,000**	**118,555,000**	**21,304,000**	**20,922,000**

Source: National Sporting Goods Association, as found in the *Statistical Abstract of the United States 1995*. Published by the Bureau of the Census, Washington, D.C., p. 260.

Look for interesting patterns in the data for males and females and in the data for the two age groups.

A. Why don't the numbers in the columns add to the given totals?

B. Write three statements that use percents to make comparisons about the numbers of male and female participants in the various activities. Explain how you found the percents.

C. Write three statements that use percents to make comparisons about the numbers of teenage and older-adult participants in the various activities.

D. Write three statements that make comparisons about the data without using percents.

You conducted a class survey at the beginning of this investigation. Now, organize the results for bicycle riding, camping, exercise walking, fishing, and swimming into a table similar to the one on page 17. Your table should have separate columns for males and females.

A. Look back at the three statements you wrote in part B of Problem 2.1 comparing the numbers of male and female participants in the various activities. Now, make the same comparisons for boys and girls in your class.

B. Compare the statements about your class data to the statements about the national data.

C. Write three statements comparing sports activities of all students in your class to those of

1. 12 to 17 year olds in the national survey

2. 55 to 64 year olds in the national survey

Arvind and Mariah tested four juice mixes.

| **Mix A** |
| 2 cups concentrate |
| 3 cups cold water |

| **Mix B** |
| 1 cup concentrate |
| 4 cups cold water |

| **Mix C** |
| 4 cups concentrate |
| 8 cups cold water |

| **Mix D** |
| 3 cups concentrate |
| 5 cups cold water |

A. Which recipe will make juice that is the most "orangey"? Explain your answer.

B. Which recipe will make juice that is the least "orangey"? Explain your answer.

C. Assume that each camper will get $\frac{1}{2}$ cup of juice. For each recipe, how much concentrate and how much water are needed to make juice for 240 campers? Explain your answer.

Suppose you are assigned to help the cook order supplies.

A. How many cans of tomatoes would you advise the cook to buy to make spaghetti for the 240 campers? Explain your answer.

B. How much would these cans of tomatoes cost altogether?

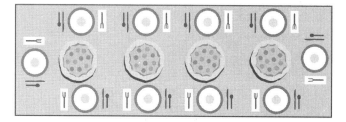
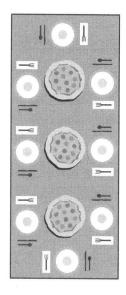

A. If the pizzas at a table are shared equally by everyone at the table, will a person sitting at a small table get the same amount of pizza as a person sitting at a large table? Explain your reasoning.

B. The ratio of large tables to small tables in the dining room is 8 to 5. There are exactly enough seats for the 240 campers. How many tables of each kind are there?

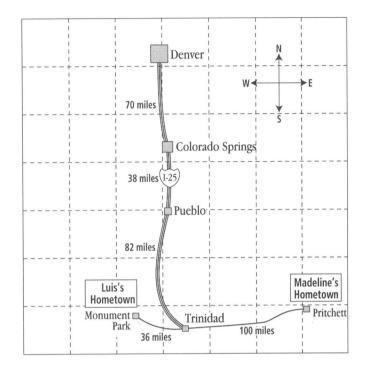

When Madeline and Luis returned from the holiday, they compared their fuel economy. Madeline's car used 19 gallons for the trip from Denver to Pritchett and back. Luis's car used only 15.5 gallons of gas for the trip from Denver to Monument Park and back. He said this proved his car was more fuel-efficient than Madeline's. Madeline disagreed. Use the gasoline and mileage data to help settle Madeline and Luis's argument.

Which car do you think is more fuel-efficient on the highway? Explain how you decided and why you think you are correct.

Madeline's car went 580 miles with 19 gallons of gasoline. Luis's car went 452 miles with 15.5 gallons of gasoline. Use this information to answer the following questions.

A. For each car, find a unit rate describing the mileage. Which car got better gas mileage? In other words, which car went more miles per gallon of gas?

B. Complete a table like the one below, showing the fuel used and the miles covered by each car based on the unit rates you found in part A. We call this kind of table a *rate table*.

Gallons of gas	0	1	2	3	4	5	6	7	8
Miles in Madeline's car									
Miles in Luis's car									

C. Look at the patterns in your table. For each car, write an equation for a rule you can use to predict the miles driven *(m)* from the gallons of gas used *(g)*.

D. Use the rules you wrote in part C to find the number of miles each car could cover if it used 9.5, 15.5, 19, 23.8, 100, 125, and 150 gallons of gasoline.

Suppose Sascha, a champion bicyclist, wants to see how far he can travel in an hour. He starts timing himself when he reaches a speed of 45 miles per hour. He maintains this speed for 10 minutes. Sascha starts to feel tired and slows down to 30 miles per hour for the next 5 minutes. He then reduces his speed to 25 miles per hour for the next 30 minutes. Finally, Sascha feels exhausted as he finishes the last 15 minutes at 15 miles per hour.

A. Make a graph showing Sascha's total distance traveled over time. Use 5-minute time intervals on the *x*-axis.

B. How far did Sascha travel in his 1-hour ride? Explain.

C. If you could maintain a steady speed of 13 miles per hour on a bike, how long would it take you to travel the same distance Sascha traveled in his 1-hour ride?

D. If you were racing Sascha, what constant (steady) speed would you have to maintain to tie him?

Craft Beads

Spheres: 12¢ for 20
Cubes: 12¢ for 15
Cylinders: 8¢ for 10

Write an equation relating the cost *(c)* and the number of beads *(x)* for each type of bead:

Spheres: $c = $ _____

Cubes: $c = $ _____

Cylinders: $c = $ _____

Sometimes the size of a crowd is estimated from aerial photographs. Imagine that the illustration below is an aerial photograph of a crowd at a rally. Each dot represents one person.

Estimate how many people attended the rally. Explain the method you used to arrive at your answer.

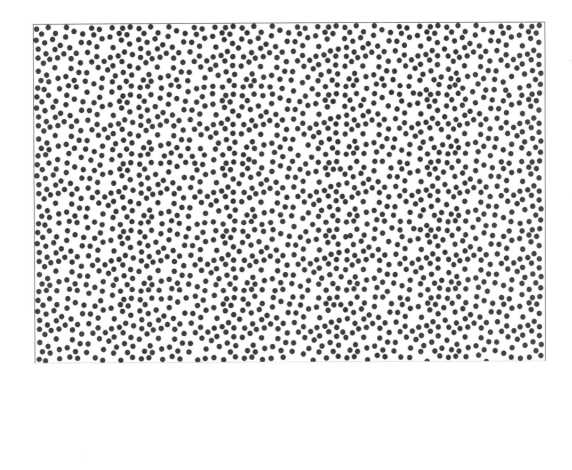

One method biologists use to count animal populations is called the *capture-tag-recapture* method. You can simulate this method by using a jar or box filled with white beans. Imagine that each bean is a deer in the upper peninsula of Michigan. Your job is to estimate the number of deer without actually counting them all.

Your group will need a container with a lid and a large number of white beans. Work with your group to perform this experiment.

- Remove about 100 beans from the container, and mark them with a pen or marker.
- Put the marked beans back into the container, and shake or mix them with the unmarked beans.
- Without looking at the beans, scoop out a handful of about 30 beans. Record the numbers of marked and unmarked beans in the sample. Return the sample to the jar, and mix the beans together again.
- Repeat this scoop-and-count procedure four more times. In each case, record the number of marked and unmarked beans.

A. Study the data you collected. Use the data to estimate the number of beans in your container. Explain how you made your estimate.

B. Based on what you have learned from this experiment, how do you think biologists count deer populations?

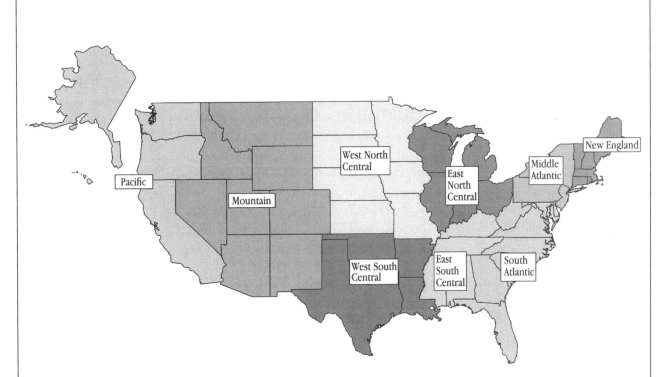

This table shows the 1994 population and land area for the nine census regions.

Region	Population	Area (square miles)
New England	13,270,000	62,811
Middle Atlantic	38,125,000	99,463
South Atlantic	46,398,000	266,221
East North Central	43,184,000	243,539
East South Central	15,890,000	178,615
West North Central	18,210,000	507,981
West South Central	28,404,000	426,234
Mountain	15,214,000	856,121
Pacific	41,645,000	895,353

Source: *Statistical Abstract of the United States 1995.* Published by the Bureau of the Census, Washington, D.C., pp. 28 and 225.

The "crowdedness" of a region is commonly reported by giving the number of people (or animals or plants) per unit of area. This rate is called the **population density** of the region.

A. What is the population density of the census region in which your school is located?

B. Divide the remaining eight census regions among the groups in your class. Find the population density of the region you are assigned. Share your group's results with the rest of the class, so that every group has data for all nine regions.

C. Order the regions from least crowded to most crowded.

D. Compare the population density of the region in which you live to the population density of each neighboring region. Write complete sentences explaining which regions you are comparing and describing how their population densities compare.

South Dakota and North Dakota rank 45 and 47 in population of all the states in the United States. South Dakota has 721,000 people in 75,896 square miles of land, and North Dakota has 638,000 people in 68,994 square miles of land.

A. Which state, North Dakota or South Dakota, has the greater population density?

B. How many citizens of one state would have to move to the other state to make the population densities in the two states equal? Explain how you arrived at your answer.

Hong Kong is reported to have the highest traffic density in the world. In 1992, there were 418 registered cars and trucks per mile of road, or about 12.63 feet per registered vehicle!

(Source: *Guinness Book of Records 1994.* Ed. Peter Matthews. New York: Bantam Books, 1994, p. 318.)

A. The city of Ole has 450,237 registered vehicles for 3000 miles of road. What is the traffic density of Ole? Calculate the number of vehicles per mile of road and the number of feet of road per vehicle.

B. The city of Driftwood Bay has 396 registered vehicles for 10 miles of road. What is the traffic density of Driftwood Bay? Calculate the number of vehicles per mile of road and the number of feet of road per vehicle.

C. Which of the three cities—Hong Kong, Ole, or Driftwood Bay—do you think is most likely to have traffic jams? Explain your answer.

D. Which of the three cities do you think is least likely to have traffic jams? Explain your answer.

T. rex weighed about 8,100 kilograms and reached heights of up to 6 meters—almost as tall as a two-story house! Archeologists have uncovered *T. rex* skulls 1 meter long and *T. rex* incisors (the longest teeth) 15 centimeters long.

A "larger than average" human being can be about 2 meters tall and weigh 90 kilograms. Human incisors are about 1 centimeter long, and a large human skull can be about 20 centimeters long.

How big was *T. rex* compared to a "larger than average" human being?

Write a paragraph to help someone younger than you understand how the size of *T. rex* compares to the size of a human. Be very specific about the comparisons you are making.

Use the table of data about the United States population to help you answer these questions.

A. How many of the 1000 delegates should be chosen from each of the nine geographic regions?

B. How many of the 1000 delegates should be from metropolitan areas, and how many should be from rural areas?

C. How many of the delegates should be of Hispanic origin?

D. Four racial groups are named in the data: white; black; Native American–Eskimo–Aleut; and Asian–Pacific Islander. How many of the total 1000 delegates should represent each of these races? How many should represent the category "all other races" (which is not mentioned in the data)?

E. Use your answers to A–D to help you develop a plan for selecting the delegates. Describe your plan in a report that you could submit to the conference organizers.

Dear Family,

The next unit in your child's course of study in mathematics class this year is *Comparing and Scaling*. The unit focuses on the concepts of ratio, proportion, and percent. Students look at problems involving many situations and learn to make comparisons using ratios, fractions, percents, and rates. Some of the questions students explore include making sense of surveys, adapting recipes for different numbers of people, analyzing sales prices, and comparing fuel economy of different cars. By the end of this unit, your child will know several powerful and useful methods for making comparisons.

You can help your child with the ideas in this unit in several ways:

- Ratios, proportions, and percents are found all around us. When you notice such a use in a newspaper or magazine, point it out to your child and discuss with your child what the numbers are telling about the situation.

- If you keep track of your car mileage, you may want to share this with your child. If you use other modes of transportation, such as a bus or subway, you may want to discuss the cost of the transportation per week, per month, and per year.

- Continue to have your child share his or her mathematics notebook with you. You may want to review the vocabulary section where your child is recording definitions for mathematical words used in this unit. If your child is struggling with any words, together you might look the words up in the dictionary or look through the unit to get a better sense of their meaning.

- Encourage your child's efforts in completing all homework assignments. Look over your child's work, and help your child make sure all questions have been answered and that all explanations are clear.

If you have any questions or concerns about this unit or your child's progress in the class, please feel free to call. We are interested in your child's success in mathematics and want to ensure that this year's mathematics experiences are enjoyable.

Sincerely,

Estimada familia,

La próxima unidad del programa de matemáticas de su hijo o hija para este curso se llama *Comparing and Scaling* (Uso de comparaciones y escalas). La misma trata principalmente sobre los conceptos de razón, proporción y porcentaje. En ella los alumnos examinar·n problemas relacionados con una diversidad de situaciones y aprenderán a hacer comparaciones usando razones, fracciones, porcentajes y tasas. En algunas de las preguntas tratarán de buscar el sentido a las encuestas, adaptar recetas de acuerdo al número de comensales, analizar precios rebajados y comparar el consumo de gasolina de distintos automóviles. Una vez finalizada la unidad, su hijo o hija conocer· varios métodos fiables y útiles para hacer comparaciones.

Para ayudar a su hijo o hija con las ideas de esta unidad, ustedes pueden hacer lo siguiente:

- Las razones, las proporciones y los porcentajes abundan en nuestro entorno. Cuando observen en un periódico o en una revista el uso de este tipo de números, háganselo notar a su hijo o hija y comenten acerca de su significado en la situación.

- Si llevan el control del número de millas que recorre su auto, será interesante que hablen sobre ello con su hijo o hija. Y si usan otros medios de transporte como, por ejemplo, el autobús o el metro, podrán hablar sobre el costo semanal, mensual y anual del mismo.

- Hagan que su hijo o hija continúe compartiendo con ustedes su cuaderno de matemáticas. Es recomendable que repasen la sección de vocabulario en la cual anota las definiciones de los términos matemáticos de la unidad. Si él o ella no consigue comprender algún término, búsquenlo juntos en el diccionario o en el contexto específico de la unidad para así entender mejor su significado.

- Anímenle a esforzarse para que complete toda la tarea. Repasen la misma y comprueben juntos que todas las preguntas han sido contestadas y que todas las explicaciones han sido escritas con claridad.

Si ustedes necesitan más detalles o aclaraciones respecto a la unidad o sobre los progresos de su hijo o hija en esta clase, no duden en llamarnos. Nos interesa que su hijo o hija avance en el estudio de las matemáticas y queremos asegurarnos de que las experiencias matemáticas que tenga este año sean lo más amenas posibles.

Atentamente,

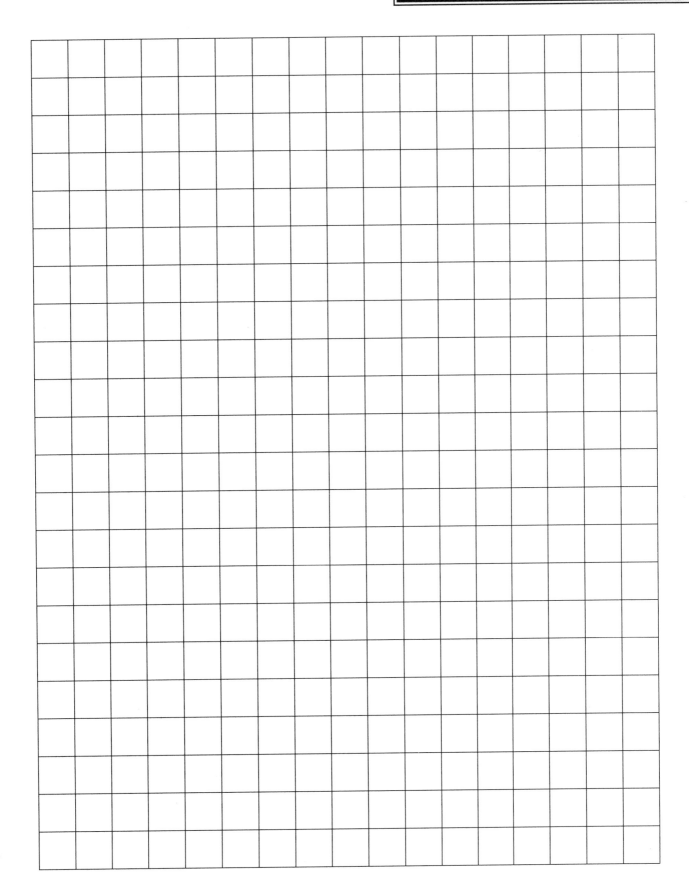

Inch Grid Paper

Additional Practice

Investigation 1

Use these problems for additional practice after Investigation 1.

In 1–5, use the table below, which shows the number of years a typical person spends engaged in various activities over a lifetime:

How We Spend Our Lives

Activity	Number of years
sleeping	$24\frac{1}{2}$
at work or school	$13\frac{1}{2}$
socializing	$4\frac{1}{2}$
watching TV	12
reading	3
eating	3
bathing and grooming	$1\frac{3}{4}$
talking on the telephone	1
miscellaneous activities*	$9\frac{1}{2}$

* Such as housekeeping, shopping, waiting in lines, walking, driving, entertainment, doing nothing.

1. According to the table, how long is a typical person's lifetime? Explain your reasoning.

2. Does a typical person spend more years watching TV or sleeping? Write a ratio that compares these two amounts.

3. The numbers of years spent doing miscellaneous activities is about how many times the number of years spent socializing?

4. Of the total number of years in a lifetime, what percent are spent sleeping? What percent are spent at work or school?

5. About what fraction of a lifetime is spent watching TV and talking on the phone? What fraction is spent in miscellaneous activities?

6. Make an interesting comparison statement about the data in the table. Tell why you think your comparison is interesting.

Investigation 2

Use these problems for additional practice after Investigation 2.

In 1 and 2, use this table, which shows the typical weight of various parts of the body for an adult weighing 152 pounds.

Body Part	Weight (pounds)
Head	10.5
Neck and Trunk	70.0
Arms	16.5
Hands	2.5
Legs	47.5
Feet	5.0

1. Estimate the percent of the total body weight each part makes up. Explain your reasoning.

2. **a.** Make a circle graph that shows the percent of the total body weight for each body part.

    b. The neck, trunk, and legs account for what total percent of the body weight?

3. Of the students in Mrs. Petonito's fourth-period math class, 16 are wearing athletic shoes, 10 are wearing boots, and 4 are wearing other kinds of shoes.

    a. What fraction of Mrs. Petonito's students are wearing boots? Explain your reasoning

    b. Suppose 1006 students attend the middle school where Mrs. Petonito teaches. Use your answer from part a to estimate the number of students in the school who are wearing boots. Explain your reasoning.

4. Of the 756 students in Chad's middle school, 44% participate in sports, 29% play in the band, and 37% take the bus to school.

    a. How many students in Chad's middle school play in the band? Explain your reasoning.

    b. How many students in Chad's middle school take the bus to school?

    c. If you add up the percents of students who play sports, play in the band, and take the bus to school, you get 110%. Explain why the percents do not add to 100%.

In 5–7, use the diagram below.

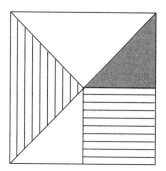

5. What fraction of the whole square is the section with vertical lines? Explain your reasoning.

6. a. What percent of the whole square are the sections with lines?

    b. If the entire square has an area of 16 cm², what would be the area of the nonwhite sections? Explain your reasoning.

7. If the white sections of the square have a combined area of 30 cm², what is the combined area of the other regions? Explain your reasoning.

In 8–10, use this table showing the numbers of endangered species throughout the world.

Numbers of Endangered Species

	United States only	United States and foreign	Foreign only
Animals	262	51	493
Plants	378	10	1
Total	**640**	**61**	**494**

8. About what fraction of the total number of endangered species are found only in foreign countries?

9. How many times more endangered plant species are there in the United States than in foreign countries? Make sure you count *all* the species of plants for each. Explain your reasoning.

Investigation 3

Use these problems for additional practice after Investigation 3.

1. Bill has a paper route in his neighborhood. It takes him 50 minutes to deliver newspapers to the 40 customers on his route.

   a. How long will it take Bill to complete his route if he adds 20 more customers in his neighborhood? Explain your reasoning.

   b. Only 30 of Bill's 40 customers take the Sunday paper. About how long does it take Bill to deliver his papers on Sundays?

2. A *micron* is a metric unit of length. There are 1 million (1,000,000) microns in 1 meter.

   a. How many microns equal 1 centimeter? Explain your reasoning.

   b. An object has a length of 2911 microns. What is the length of the object in centimeters?

   c. An object has a width of 0.000351 meters. What is the width of the object in microns?

   d. Which metric unit—meters, centimeters, or microns—do you think is best to use to express the length of your pencil? Explain your reasoning.

3. Betty and Derek are making punch for a class party. The directions on the liquid punch mix say to use 3 cups of mix for every 7 cups of water. Betty and Derek want to make enough punch so that each of the 25 people at the party can have 2 cups.

   a. How many cups of punch mix will Betty and Derek need to use? Explain your reasoning.

   b. How many cups of water will Betty and Derek need to use?

   c. Betty and Derek want to put the punch in bowls that hold 20 cups each. How many bowls will they need?

In 4–7, use the diagram below.

4. What is the ratio of the area of the trapezoid to the area of the hexagon? Explain your reasoning.

5. What is the ratio of the area of the large triangle to the area of the hexagon? Explain your reasoning.

6. If the area of the hexagon is 24 square units, what is the area of the trapezoid? What is the area of the large triangle? Explain your reasoning.

7. If the area of the trapezoid is 4 square units, what is the area of the large triangle?

Investigation 4

Use these problems for additional practice after Investigation 4.

1. Tony can type at a constant rate of 55 words per minute.

   a. Write an equation for the number of words, W, Tony can type in T minutes.

   b. How many words can Tony type in 20 minutes?

   c. If Tony has a half hour to type a 1600-word essay, will he have time to type the entire essay? Explain your reasoning.

2. The students in the Metropolis Middle School band held a car wash to help raise money for new uniforms.

   a. The students washed 68 cars in seven hours. Estimate the rate at which they washed the cars. Explain your reasoning.

   b. The students raised $408 from washing the 68 cars. How much did the students charge for washing a car?

   c. There are 41 students in the band. Estimate the money earned per student from the car wash. Explain your reasoning.

3. Sharnel needs to replace all eight wheels on her in-line skates. She can buy replacement wheels for $2.19 each at Roller-Go Sports, for $5.95 for a pack of three wheels at Discount Sports, or for $9.25 for a pack of four wheels at Pro-Sports.

   a. What is the cost per wheel at each of the three stores? Explain your reasoning.

   b. If Sharnel is willing to go to all three stores, what combination of purchases will result in Sharnel having exactly eight wheels for the lowest cost? Explain your reasoning.

   c. If Sharnel has time to visit only one store to buy her wheels, which store should she go to? Explain your reasoning.

4. Mr. Johnson sells trophies by their height. He charges a fixed price per centimeter. A short trophy measures 15 centimeters and sells for $4.50.

   a. A taller trophy sells for $6.00. How tall is the $6.00 trophy?

   b. Another trophy is 35 centimeters tall. How much does this trophy cost?

5. A veterinarian's clinic has a patient load of 150 cats and dogs. The ratio of cats to dogs is 4 to 8. How many patients are cats and how many are dogs? Explain your reasoning.

6. On a map, 1 centimeter = 50 kilometers. What is the actual distance between two towns that are $3\frac{1}{2}$ centimeters apart on the map? Explain your reasoning.

Investigation 5

Use these problems for additional practice after Investigation 5.

1. Joe-Ellen wants to estimate the number of red chips in a bag of 300 red, white, and blue chips. She gathers some data by taking samples. Use her data to predict the number of red chips in the bag.

Sample 1
Number of red chips: 9
Number of chips in sample: 25

Sample 2
Number of red chips: 23
Number of chips in sample: 50

Sample 3
Number of red chips: 11
Number of chips in sample: 30

Sample 4
Number of red chips: 19
Number of chips in sample: 45

In 2–3, use the table below.

Population and Land Area of Selected States

State	Population	Area (square miles)
California	31,431,000	155,973
Connecticut	3,275,000	4845
New Hampshire	1,137,000	8969
North Dakota	638,000	68,994
South Dakota	721,000	75,896
Vermont	580,000	9249
Wyoming	476,000	97,105

Source: *Statistical Abstract of the United States 1995.* Published by the
Bureau of the Census, Washington, D.C., pp. 28 and 225.

2. How many people would have to move from New Hampshire to Vermont to make the population densities in the two states the same? Explain your reasoning.

3. **a.** If all the people in Connecticut moved to New Hampshire, what would be the population density of New Hampshire?

   b. If all the people in New Hampshire moved to Connecticut, what would be the population density of Connecticut?

4. In 1994, Alpha College had a student enrollment of 1334 and a total of 1.98×10^5 books in its library. In the same year, Beta College had a student enrollment of 1674 and a total of 3.9×10^5 books in its library. The number of library books per student is the *book to student density* of the college.

   a. Without doing any calculations, determine which college had a higher book to student density in 1994. Explain your reasoning.

   b. Describe two ways the college with the lower book to student density could change its book to student density to equal that of the other college. Explain your reasoning.

   c. Of the two approaches for raising the book to student density at the college in part b, write two or three sentences explaining which of the approaches you would recommend to the college and why.

5. Of the 2159 students who attend Gamma College, 57% are from rural areas, 26% are from suburban areas, and 17% are from urban areas.

   a. How many students at Gamma College are from rural areas?

   b. How many students at Gamma College are from urban areas?

   c. Next year, the enrollment of Gamma College will increase to 2471, with 650 students coming from suburban areas. Do you think this is a major change in the portion of students from suburban areas? Explain your reasoning.

Investigation 6

Use these problems for additional practice after Investigation 6.

1. Ellen and her stepfather are replacing the carpet in the living room. They measure the room and find that the area is 24 yd^2. They go to their local Carpet Pile store to purchase the new carpet.

    a. Upon arriving at Carpet Pile, Ellen and her stepfather find that the carpet they want is measured in square feet, not square yards. How many square feet are there in a square yard? Draw a diagram to explain your reasoning.

    b. How many square feet of carpet will Ellen and her stepfather need to carpet the living room?

2. Josh jogs an average of 8 miles per week for three weeks. How many miles will he need to jog during the fourth week to bring his four-week average to 10 miles per week?

3. Kyle has maintained a consistent batting average of .350 on the Metropolis Middle School baseball team during the first half of the season. Assuming his batting average stays the same for the rest of the season, write and solve proportions to answer these questions:

    a. How many hits will Kyle make in his next 20 times at bat?

    b. How many hits will Kyle make in his next 35 times at bat?

    c. How many times at bat will it take Kyle to make 10 hits?

    d. How many times at bat will it take Kyle to make 18 hits?

Investigation 4

1. a. $W = 55 \times T$

    b. $55 \times 20 = 1100$ words

    c. yes; Tony can type 1650 words in 30 minutes.

2. a. The students washed about 10 cars per hour, because 10 cars per hour for seven hours would be 70 cars, which is just over the 68 cars actually washed.

    b. The students charged $\frac{\$408}{68} = \$6$ per car.

    c. Each student earned about $10 for uniforms from the car wash. 41 students earning an average of $10 each would raise $410, which is just slightly more than the $408 actually raised.

3. a. Roller-Go: $2.19 per wheel

    Discount Sports: $5.95 ÷ 3 = $1.98 per wheel

    Pro-Sports: $9.25 ÷ 4 = $2.31 per wheel

    b. She can buy two packages of 3 wheels at $5.95 each and 2 single wheels at $2.19 each, for a total of $16.28

    c. Buying the single wheels at $2.19 each is the least expensive if she can go to only one store.

4. a. Trophies cost $4.50 ÷ 15 cm = $0.30 per centimeter, so the trophy is 6.00 ÷ 0.30 = 20 centimeters tall.

    b. The trophy costs $35 \times 0.30 = \$10.50$.

5. Out of 12 animals, the ratio of cats is $\frac{4}{12}$, or $\frac{1}{3}$, and the ratio of dogs is $\frac{8}{12}$, or $\frac{2}{3}$. So $\frac{1}{3}$ of the 150 animals, or 50 animals, are cats, and $\frac{2}{3}$, or 100 animals, are dogs.

6. $3\frac{1}{2} \times 50 = 175$ km

Investigation 5

1. Adding the data from the samples, we find that 62 of the 150 chips are red. This is about 40%, so we might predict that 40% of the 300 chips, or 120 chips, are red.

2. By combining the data for the two states, we get an overall population density of
    $\frac{1{,}717{,}000 \text{ people}}{18{,}218 \text{ mi}^2} \approx 94$ people per mi^2.
    For New Hampshire to have this population density, about $8969 \times 94 = 843{,}086$ people would have to live there. So, $1{,}137{,}000 - 843{,}086 = 293{,}914$ people would have to move from New Hampshire to Vermont.

3. a. $\frac{3{,}275{,}000 + 1{,}137{,}000}{8969} \approx 492$ people per mi^2

    b. $\frac{3{,}275{,}000 + 1{,}137{,}000}{4845} \approx 911$ people per mi^2

4. a. Beta College has a higher book to student density because Beta College had twice as many books as Alpha College but fewer than twice as many students.

    b. It could increase the number of books in the library or decrease the number of students.

    c. Answers will vary. Realistically, increasing the number of books in the library is the most reasonable course of action. Decreasing the number of students would mean less tuition and revenue for Alpha College.

5.   **a.** $0.57 \times 2159 = 1231$

    b. $0.17 \times 2159 = 367$

    c. $\frac{650}{2471} = 0.26 = 26\%$ will be from suburban areas. The data do not indicate a significant change in the number of students from suburban areas.

Investigation 6

1.   **a.** There are 9 ft^2 in 1 yd^2.

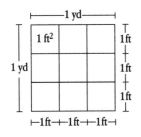

    b. $24 \times 9 = 216$ ft^2

2. For Josh to have a four-week average of 10 miles per week, he will need to jog a total of 40 miles. Since he has jogged $3 \times 8 = 24$ miles for the first three weeks, Josh will need to jog $40 - 24 = 16$ miles during the fourth week.

3. A batting average of .350 is a ratio of $\frac{35}{100}$.

    a. $\frac{35}{100} = \frac{\text{hits}}{20}$; Kyle will make 7 hits.

    b. $\frac{35}{100} = \frac{\text{hits}}{35}$; Kyle will make 12 hits.

    c. $\frac{35}{100} = \frac{10}{\text{at bats}}$; Kyle would need 29 at bats.

    d. $\frac{35}{100} = \frac{18}{\text{at bats}}$; Kyle would need 52 at bats.

population density The population density is the average number of things (people, animals, and so on) per unit of area (or, less commonly, the average amount of space per person or animal). Population density indicates how crowded a region is and can be calculated as the ratio population/area.

proportion An equation stating that two ratios are equal. For example:

$$\frac{\text{hours spent on homework}}{\text{hours spent in school}} = \frac{2}{7}$$

Note that this does not necessarily imply that "hours spent on homework" equals 2, nor that "hours spent in school" equals 7. During a week 10 hours may have been spent on homework, while 35 hours were spent in school. The proportion is still true because $\frac{10}{35} = \frac{2}{7}$.

rate A comparison of the measurements of two different units or objects is called a rate. A rate can be thought of as a direct comparison of two sets (20 cookies for 5 children) or as an average amount (4 cookies per child). A rate such as 5.5 miles per hour can be written in several ways: $\frac{5.5 \text{ miles}}{1 \text{ hour}}$, or 5.5 miles : 1 hour, or $\frac{1 \text{ hour}}{5.5 \text{ miles}}$

ratio A ratio is a comparison of two quantities that tells the scale between them. Ratios may be expressed as quotients, fractions, decimals, percents, or given in the form *a:b*. Here are some examples of uses of ratios:

- The ratio of the length of a side of the small figure in a pair of similar figures to the corresponding side in the large figure is $\frac{1}{2}$. The ratio of the length of the sides in the large figure to the corresponding sides in the small figure is $\frac{2}{1}$, or 2.

- The ratio of females to males on the swim team is 2 to 3, or $\frac{2 \text{ females}}{3 \text{ males}}$.

- The train travels at a speed of 80 miles per hour, or $\frac{80 \text{ miles}}{1 \text{ hour}}$.

- If a small figure is enlarged by a scale factor of 2, the new figure will have an area four times its original size. The ratio of the small figure's area to the large figure's area will be $\frac{1}{4}$. The ratio of the large figure's area to the small figure's area will be $\frac{4}{1}$ or 4.

scale, scaling The scale is the number a ratio is multiplied by to find an equivalent ratio. Scaling a ratio produces any number of equivalent ratios, which all have the same units and the same average distribution. For example, multiplying the rate of 4.5 gallons per hour by a scale of 2 yields the rate of 9 gallons per 2 hours. Scales are also used on maps to give the relationship between a measurement on the map to the actual physical measurement.

unit rate A unit rate compares an amount to a single unit. For example, 1.9 children per family, 32 mpg, and $\frac{3 \text{ flavors of ice cream}}{1 \text{ banana split}}$ are unit rates. Unit rates are often found by scaling other rates.

Index

Index